MANDELSTAM THEORY AND REGGE POLES

Frontiers in Physics

A Lecture Note and Reprint Series

DAVID PINES, ***Editor***

P. W. Anderson **CONCEPTS IN SOLIDS:** *Lectures on the Theory of Solids*

N. Bloembergen **NUCLEAR MAGNETIC RELAXATION:** *A Reprint Volume*

Geoffrey F. Chew **S-MATRIX THEORY OF STRONG INTERACTIONS:** *A Lecture Note and Reprint Volume*

R. P. Feynman **QUANTUM ELECTRODYNAMICS:** *A Lecture Note and Reprint Volume*

R. P. Feynman **THE THEORY OF FUNDAMENTAL PROCESSES:** *A Lecture Note Volume*

Hans Frauenfelder **THE MÖSSBAUER EFFECT:** *A Collection of Reprints with an Introduction*

Robert Hofstadter **NUCLEAR AND NUCLEON STRUCTURE:** *A Reprint Volume*

Leo P. Kadanoff and Gordon Baym **QUANTUM STATISTICAL MECHANICS:** *A Lecture Note Volume*

A. M. Lane **RECENT DEVELOPMENTS IN NUCLEAR THEORY:** *A Lecture Note and Reprint Volume*

R. Omnès and M. Froissart **MANDELSTAM THEORY AND REGGE POLES:** *An Introduction for Experimentalists*

George E. Pake **PARAMAGNETIC RESONANCE:** *An Introductory Monograph*

David Pines **THE MANY-BODY PROBLEM:** *A Lecture Note and Reprint Volume*

E. J. Squires **COMPLEX ANGULAR MOMENTA AND PARTICLE PHYSICS:** *A Lecture Note and Reprint Volume*

L. Van Hove, N. M. Hugenholtz, and L. P. Howland **PROBLEMS IN THE QUANTUM THEORY OF MANY-PARTICLE SYSTEMS:** *A Reprint Volume*

MANDELSTAM THEORY AND REGGE POLES

AN INTRODUCTION FOR EXPERIMENTALISTS

★

R. OMNÈS
Institut des Hautes Études Scientifiques

M. FROISSART
Centre d'Études Nucléaires de Saclay

W. A. BENJAMIN, INC.
1963 New York Amsterdam

MANDELSTAM THEORY AND REGGE POLES
An Introduction for Experimentalists

Library of Congress Catalog Card Number: 63-22795
Manufactured in the United States of America

The final manuscript was received on July 1, 1963; this volume was published December 15, 1963

The publisher is pleased to acknowledge the assistance of Zeb Delaire, who composed the volume; Cecilia Duray-Bito, who produced the illustrations; and William Prokos, who designed the dust jacket

W. A. BENJAMIN, INC.
New York, New York

EDITOR'S FOREWORD

The problem of communicating in a coherent fashion the recent developments in the most exciting and active fields of physics seems particularly pressing today. The enormous growth in the number of physicists has tended to make the familiar channels of communication considerably less effective. It has become increasingly difficult for experts in a given field to keep up with the current literature; the novice can only be confused. What is needed is both a consistent account of a field and the presentation of a definite "point of view" concerning it. Formal monographs cannot meet such a need in a rapidly developing field, and, perhaps more important, the review article seems to have fallen into disfavor. Indeed, it would seem that the people most actively engaged in developing a given field are the people least likely to write at length about it.

"Frontiers in Physics" has been conceived in an effort to improve the situation in several ways. First, to take advantage of the fact that the leading physicists today frequently give a series of lectures, a graduate seminar, or a graduate course in their special fields of interest. Such lectures serve to summarize the present status of a rapidly developing field and may well constitute the only coherent account available at the time. Often, notes on lectures exist (prepared by the lecturer himself, by graduate students, or by postdoctoral fellows) and have been distributed in mimeographed form on a limited basis. One of the principal purposes of the "Frontiers in Physics" series is to make such notes available to a wider audience of physicists.

It should be emphasized that lecture notes are necessarily rough and informal, both in style and content, and those in the series will prove no exception. This is as it should be. The point of the series is to offer new, rapid, more informal, and, it is hoped, more effective ways for physicists to teach one another. The point is lost if only elegant notes qualify.

A second way to improve communication in very active fields of physics is by the publication of collections of reprints of recent articles. Such collections are themselves useful to people working in the field. The value of the reprints would, however, seem much enhanced if the collection would be accompanied by an introduction of moderate length, which would serve to tie the collection together and, necessarily, constitute a brief survey of the present status of the field. Again, it is appropriate that such an introduction be informal, in keeping with the active character of the field.

A third possibility for the series might be called an informal monograph, to connote the fact that it represents an intermediate step between lecture notes and formal monographs. It would offer the author an opportunity to present his views of a field that has developed to the point at which a summation might prove extraordinarily fruitful, but for which a formal monograph might not be feasible or desirable.

Fourth, there are the contemporary classics—papers or lectures which constitute a particularly valuable approach to the teaching and learning of physics today. Here one thinks of fields that lie at the heart of much of present-day research, but whose essentials are by now well understood, such as quantum electrodynamics or magnetic resonance. In such fields some of the best pedagogical material is not readily available, either because it consists of papers long out of print or lectures that have never been published.

"Frontiers in Physics" is designed to be flexible in editorial format. Authors are encouraged to use as many of the foregoing approaches as seem desirable for the project at hand. The publishing format for the series is in keeping with its intentions. Photo-offset printing is used throughout, and the books are paperbound, in order to speed publication and reduce costs. It is hoped that the books will thereby be within the financial reach of graduate students in this country and abroad.

Finally, because the series represents something of an experiment on the part of the editor and the publisher, suggestions from interested readers as to format, contributors, and contributions will be most welcome.

David Pines

Urbana, Illinois
August 1961

PREFACE

The present book stems from separate lecture courses given by the authors at Professor Leprince-Ringuet's laboratory in the École Polytechnique and at Saclay. As the audience was essentially made up of experimentalists, these courses were of a descriptive character.

The book is addressed to students who are not acquainted with the most recent work in the theory of strongly interacting elementary particles. Our aim has been to extract the most important physical ideas, with proofs frequently omitted or replaced by heuristic arguments. The level has been kept as elementary as possible; the reader is assumed to know only elementary quantum mechanics. We have made no attempts at mathematical rigor or completeness, since further developments may be found in the book by G. F. Chew, *S-Matrix Theory of Strong Interactions,* published in the same series.

As is customary in elementary textbooks, we have not explicitly referred to the original authors of the work under description. We feel justified in not doing so because our heuristic presentation would hardly give them due credit. In addition, we have given only a short bibliography, intended to provide a reading program for those who may want to acquaint themselves further with the subject.

One of the authors (R. O.) thanks Mr. L. Motchane for his hospitality at the Institut des Hautes Études Scientifiques. We both thank Mlle Helene Noir for her invaluable aid in preparing the manuscript.

R. Omnès
M. Froissart

Paris, France
September 1963

CONTENTS

1

NONRELATIVISTIC SCATTERING THEORY

1-1 FORMULATION OF THE PROBLEM

We shall be mainly concerned with collision problems and, more precisely, scattering problems. In order to perform a scattering experiment, one generally uses a beam of particles coming, for instance, from an accelerator. These particles have momenta ranging around some mean value $\mathbf{k}$ and they constitute a packet whose position is more or less well-defined in space. This packet travels, deforming itself as time goes on, since the particles do not have quite the same velocity, until it hits a target. Some particles collide with the atoms or the nuclei of the target while some others pass without suffering any interaction. The first group is scattered in all directions, as a cloud diverging from the target, the second group continues traveling in the same direction as the initial packet.

In some instances, one has to deal not with such a beam of many particles, but with only one particle. That is the case, for instance, in a bubble-chamber experiment, where one can get a photographic picture of the trajectory of an individual particle. However, the quantum-mechanical description of such an experiment, being statistical in its character, does not differ essentially from our preceding description of the history of a many-particle bunch. Now we shall say that the wave function $\varphi(\mathbf{x},t)$ of the initial particle obeys the free-particle Schrödinger equation:

$$i\hbar \frac{\partial \varphi}{\partial t} = -\frac{\hbar^2}{2m} \nabla^2 \varphi(\mathbf{x},t) \qquad (1\text{-}1)$$

$\varphi(\mathbf{x},t)$ is in fact a superposition of plane waves whose momenta range around a mean value $\mathbf{k}$, and it is localized as a wave packet of a finite extension. This packet travels, deforming itself until it hits a target. At this point, we have to take into account the interaction between the particle and the target (for instance, a nucleon) by introducing a localized potential so that the Schrödinger equation now reads

$$i\hbar \frac{\partial \varphi}{\partial t} = -\frac{\hbar^2}{2m} \nabla^2 \varphi(\mathbf{x},t) + V(\mathbf{x})\varphi(\mathbf{x},t) \tag{1-2}$$

After a long time has elapsed, the probability density of the particle inside the target has gone to zero, and $\varphi(\mathbf{x},t)$ again satisfies the free-particle Schrödinger equation (1-1), but it is split in two parts: a first one, analogous to the initial wave packet, is a superposition of plane waves whose momenta range around $\mathbf{k}$, its total probability, however, being less than that of the incoming packet. A second part is made up of outgoing spherical waves whose momenta range in absolute values around $|\mathbf{k}|$ and which looks like an exploding cloud. Their total probability is the scattering probability of the incoming packet. As the time of the collision was more or less well defined, the outgoing wave cloud, which was emitted at that time, will be localized in space and its radius will expand with a velocity k/m. As its probability (i.e., $\int |\varphi^2$ cloud $| d^3x$) will stay constant after emission, its wave function has to decrease like the inverse radius as this radius increases.

It is possible to give a complete mathematical analysis of this behavior of a wave packet. However, it will be simpler, from a purely mathematical standpoint, to replace the incoming packet by a pure plane wave. The price to pay for such a simplification is that momentum and energy are then absolutely defined, and it is no longer possible to follow the scattering process in space and time. We must then use the time-independent Schrödinger equation which will be satisfied by the total wave function $\Psi(\mathbf{x})$:

$$\nabla^2 \Psi(\mathbf{x}) + [k^2 - V(\mathbf{x})]\Psi(\mathbf{x}) = 0 \tag{1-3}$$

(here we have used $E = k^2/2m$ and, for simplicity, we have chosen a system of units such that the mass of the particle is 1/2 and $\hbar = 1$). For values of $\mathbf{x}$ corresponding to points outside the target, i.e., such that the potential is zero, $\Psi(\mathbf{x})$ will satisfy the free-particle Schrödinger equation. Moreover we have seen that the wave function, in that exterior region, may consist of three parts:

a. A plane wave corresponding to the incoming packet.

b. Another plane wave, with the same momentum, corresponding to the part of the incoming packet that did not suffer collision.

c. An outgoing wave corresponding to scattered particles.

The two plane waves, in a time-independent theory, cannot be separated and join to form a single, say $e^{i\mathbf{k}\cdot\mathbf{x}}$. As for the outgoing wave, we know that the absolute value of its momentum is k and that it decreases like 1/r; thus it has necessarily the form

$$f(\theta,\varphi)\frac{e^{ikr}}{r} \qquad r = |\mathbf{x}|$$

for large enough values of r. Here we have introduced a spherical coordinate system whose axis is directed along the incoming momentum. In the most frequent case, the potential depends only on r, and particles will be scattered just as often in any two directions, making the same angle θ with the incoming momentum, so that $f(\theta,\varphi)$ will depend only on θ. This function $f(\theta,\varphi)$ or $f(\theta)$ is called the scattering amplitude.

It is easy to relate the scattering amplitude and the scattering cross section. In fact, the incoming wave function $e^{i\mathbf{k}\cdot\mathbf{x}}$ corresponds to a unit density, and to a flux equal to the velocity 2k of incoming particles, while the number of particles per unit time scattered in the solid angle $d\Omega$ around θ is equal to $2k\,|f(\theta)r^{-1}|^2\, r^2\, d\Omega = 2k\,|f|^2\, d\Omega$. By definition, the scattering cross section $d\sigma$ for this process is the ratio of the number of events by the incoming flux, or

$$\frac{d\sigma}{d\Omega} = |f(\theta)|^2 \tag{1-4}$$

Let us now see how we shall formulate a scattering problem: Find a solution $\Psi(\mathbf{x})$ of the time-independent Schrödinger equation (1-3), behaving, for large-enough values of $\mathbf{x}$, as

$$\Psi(\mathbf{x}) = e^{i\mathbf{k}\cdot\mathbf{x}} + f(\theta)\frac{e^{ikr}}{r} + 0\left(\frac{1}{r^2}\right) \tag{1-5}$$

By $0(1/r^2)$ we mean a quantity which goes to zero at least as fast as r^{-2} when r goes to infinity. The ultimate goal of the problem is in fact to determine from $\Psi(\mathbf{x})$ the exact form of the scattering amplitude $f(\theta)$, which is the interesting quantity, since it gives the scattering cross section through (1-4).

In the following paragraphs, we shall cast that problem into an integral form more suited to analysis. In particular, we shall obtain a series expansion solution for $\Psi(\mathbf{x})$ which is known as the Born series. This series, besides being very useful in practical calculations, has a physical interpretation which gives a new insight into the scattering process. Then we shall obtain equations determining the scattering amplitude directly, without having to pass through the wave-function calculation as an intermediate step.

1-2 INTEGRAL FORM OF THE SCHRÖDINGER EQUATION

It is possible to cast the Schrodinger equation (1-3) together with the boundary condition (1-5) into a single integral equation. Let us first find it in a formal way.

Together with the complete Schrödinger equation (1-3) we can introduce the free-particle Schrödinger equation satisfied by the plane-wave part of the wave function

$$(\nabla^2 + k^2)e^{i\mathbf{k}\cdot\mathbf{x}} = 0 \tag{1-6}$$

Subtracting (1-6) from (1-3) we get an equation which determines the behavior of $\Psi(x) - e^{i\mathbf{k}\cdot\mathbf{x}}$, i.e., the nontrivial part of the wave function, which we shall call the "scattered wave function." That equation reads

$$(\nabla^2 + k^2)[\Psi(\mathbf{x}) - e^{i\mathbf{k}\cdot\mathbf{x}}] = V(\mathbf{x})\,\Psi(\mathbf{x}) \tag{1-7}$$

Now, suppose that, quite formally, we can define an inverse operator of the differential operator $\nabla^2 + k^2$, which we shall denote by $(\nabla^2 + k^2)^{-1}$. Multiplying both sides of (1-7) by that operator we get

$$\Psi(\mathbf{x}) = e^{i\mathbf{k}\cdot\mathbf{x}} + \frac{1}{\nabla^2 + k^2}\,V(\mathbf{x})\,\Psi(\mathbf{x}) \tag{1-8}$$

The operator $(\nabla^2 + k^2)^{-1}$ must now be defined properly in order not to write nonsense. In fact it has up to now been given only a strictly abstract meaning. To be more precise, consider a physical state represented by a Dirac ket $|\alpha\rangle$ in an abstract form. We know that we can realize that ket as a wave function $\phi_\alpha(\mathbf{x})$ in $\mathbf{x}$ space. The operator $(\hbar/i)\nabla$ in x space realizes then the abstract momentum operator $\mathbf{P}$, and $\nabla^2 + k^2$ realizes the abstract operator $k^2 - \mathbf{P}^2$. What we have introduced is the abstract operator $(k^2 - \mathbf{P}^2)^{-1}$. Our question will now be: how to write $(k^2 - \mathbf{P}^2)^{-1}$ as an explicit operator acting on the wave function $\phi_\alpha(\mathbf{x})$, $|\alpha\rangle$ being any arbitrary state?

To answer that question it will be useful to represent states $|\alpha\rangle$ not only as wave functions $\phi_\alpha(\mathbf{x})$ in $\mathbf{x}$ space but also as wave functions $\phi_\alpha(\mathbf{p})$ in momentum space. This is in fact suggested by the simple relation of our operator to the momentum operator. Thus let us introduce the set of eigenstates $|\mathbf{p}\rangle$ of the momentum operator $\mathbf{P}$, that is, states satisfying

$$\mathbf{P}\,|\mathbf{p}\rangle = \mathbf{p}\,|\mathbf{p}\rangle$$

$|\mathbf{p}\rangle$ is realized in $\mathbf{x}$ space by the wave function $e^{i\mathbf{p}\cdot\mathbf{x}}$. When acting on $|\mathbf{p}\rangle$, the operator $(k^2 - \mathbf{P}^2)^{-1}$ gives

$$(k^2 - \mathbf{P}^2)^{-1} \,|\mathbf{p}\rangle = (k^2 - \mathbf{p}^2)^{-1} \,|\mathbf{p}\rangle \tag{1-9}$$

and we see that $(\nabla^2 + k^2)^{-1}$ is well defined, except when we want to apply it to states corresponding to values of $\mathbf{p}$ such that $\mathbf{p}^2 = k^2$. Let us momentarily neglect that indeterminacy and translate (1-9) into $\mathbf{x}$ space. To do so, we shall use the obvious relation

$$\sum_{\mathbf{p}} |\mathbf{p}\rangle\langle\mathbf{p}| = \underline{1}$$

where the summation goes over all possible values of $\mathbf{p}$, and $\underline{1}$ represents the identity operator. Then

$$(k^2 - \mathbf{P}^2)^{-1} \,|\alpha\rangle = (k^2 - \mathbf{P}^2)^{-1} \sum |\mathbf{p}\rangle\langle\mathbf{p}|\alpha\rangle$$

$$= \sum_{\mathbf{p}} \frac{1}{k^2 - \mathbf{p}^2} \langle\mathbf{p}|\alpha\rangle\,|\mathbf{p}\rangle \tag{1-10}$$

In order to translate (1-10) into $\mathbf{x}$ space, we shall replace $|\mathbf{p}\rangle$ by the corresponding wave function $e^{i\mathbf{p}\cdot\mathbf{x}}$ and $\langle\mathbf{p}|\alpha\rangle$ by its explicit form $\int e^{-i\mathbf{p}\cdot\mathbf{y}}\, \varphi_\alpha(\mathbf{y})\, d^3y$ so that we shall get

$$(\nabla^2 + k^2)^{-1} \varphi_\alpha(\mathbf{x})$$

$$= \int \frac{d^3p}{(2\pi)^3} \frac{1}{k^2 - \mathbf{p}^2} e^{i\mathbf{p}\cdot\mathbf{x}} \int e^{-i\mathbf{p}\cdot\mathbf{y}} \varphi_\alpha(\mathbf{y})\, d^3y$$

where we have written the summation over eigenvalues of the momentum as an integration. That is most trivially done by supposing everything to be quantized in a unit volume so that the density of states is simply $(2\pi)^{-3}$. We have thus got

$$(\nabla^2 + k^2)^{-1} \varphi_\alpha(\mathbf{x}) = \int G(\mathbf{x} - \mathbf{y})\, \varphi_\alpha(\mathbf{y})\, d^3y \tag{1-11}$$

where the function $G(\mathbf{x})$ (the so-called Green's function) is defined as

$$G(\mathbf{x}) = \frac{1}{(2\pi)^3} \int e^{i\mathbf{p}\cdot\mathbf{x}} \frac{d^3p}{k^2 - \mathbf{p}^2} \tag{1-12}$$

We must now compute that integral. That is not a trivial task, for it is not well defined, the integrand being infinite for $\mathbf{p}^2 = k^2$. However, it may be remarked that, up to this point, we have only used the Schrödinger equation (1-3) without considering the boundary condition (1-5). In fact, if we compare (1-8) and the condition (1-5) we see that the "scattered wave function," which is obtained by suppressing the initial plane-wave function $e^{i\mathbf{k}\cdot\mathbf{x}}$ from the complete wave function $\Psi(\mathbf{x})$, has to behave as a purely outgoing spherical wave for large values of $|\mathbf{x}|$. It will be necessary to use that physical condition in order to give a completely definite meaning to $(\nabla^2 + k^2)^{-1}$, i.e., to the integral in (1-12).

Let us first dispose of the angular variables. It is obvious from (1-12) that $G(\mathbf{x})$ does not change under a rotation, so that it is only a function of $r = |\mathbf{x}|$. We can thus choose $\mathbf{x}$ in a definite direction which we shall take as the z axis, replacing $e^{i\mathbf{p}\cdot\mathbf{x}}$ by $e^{ipr\cos\alpha}$, α being the angle between the direction of $\mathbf{p}$ and the z axis. We can integrate on the second angle which defines, together with α, the direction of $\mathbf{p}$ in spherical coordinates. In fact, this integration amounts to a multiplication by 2π, so that we get

$$G(r) = \frac{1}{(2\pi)^2} \int e^{ipr\cos\alpha} \frac{p^2\, dp\, d\cos\alpha}{k^2 - p^2} \tag{1-13}$$

The integration over $\cos\alpha$ is easy and gives

$$G(r) = \frac{1}{2\pi^2} \int_0^{\infty} \frac{\sin pr}{r} \frac{p\, dp}{k^2 - p^2} \tag{1-14}$$

or, using the symmetry of the integrand with respect to the transformation of p in $-p$,

$$G(r) = \frac{1}{4\pi^2} \int_{-\infty}^{+\infty} \frac{\sin pr}{r} \frac{p\, dp}{k^2 - p^2} \tag{1-15}$$

As our physical condition is that $G(r)$ ensures the outgoing character of the scattered wave function, it is natural to split the integrand in its outgoing and ingoing parts, i.e., to replace $\sin pr$ by $(2i)^{-1}(e^{ipr} - e^{-ipr})$. If, on the other hand, we use

$$\frac{p}{k^2 - p^2} = -\frac{1}{2}\left[\frac{1}{p-k} + \frac{1}{p+k}\right]$$

we get

$$G(r) = -\frac{1}{8\pi^2 r} \int_{-\infty}^{+\infty} \frac{e^{ipr}\, dp}{2i} \left[\frac{1}{p-k} + \frac{1}{p+k}\right]$$

$$+ \frac{1}{8\pi^2 r} \int_{-\infty}^{+\infty} \frac{e^{-ipr}\, dp}{2i} \left[\frac{1}{p-k} + \frac{1}{p+k}\right] \tag{1-16}$$

Let us stick to the second integral. It is in fact not well defined, since the integration path, going along the real axis, passes through the two poles $p = \pm k$ of the integrand. It is, however, possible to give it a well-defined meaning by considering it as an integral in the complex plane of p and, in place of integrating along the real axis, integrating along one of the four paths L_1, L_2, L_3, L_4 of Fig. 1-1, which differ by the way they pass around the two poles. In each of these cases we can compute the integral by using contour integration. In fact, it is clear that e^{-ipr} goes to zero exponentially when p is a complex number $p = p_1 - ip_2$ and p_2 tends to $+\infty$, since then the modulus of e^{-ipr} is $e^{-p_2 r}$.

Thus, the integral of the integrand of the second term in (1-16) along the large semicircular contour C in the lower half of the complex p plane will tend to zero as the radius of C increases. Consequently we can add that integral along C to the integrals along L_1, L_2, L_3, or L_4 without changing their values. These integrals will then be equal to $-2\pi i$ times the residues of the poles enclosed in the contours formed by C and L_1, for instance; the minus sign comes from the fact that we are integrating around the contours in a clockwise direction. Hence we get for the last term in (1-16)

integrated along L_1: $-\dfrac{1}{8\pi r}\left[e^{-ikr} + e^{ikr}\right]$

integrated along L_2: 0

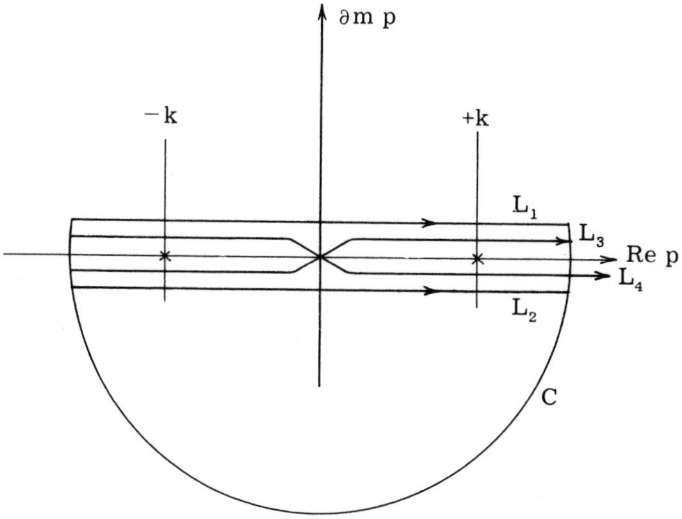

Figure 1-1

integrated along L_3: $-\frac{1}{8\pi r}\, e^{-ikr}$

integrated along L_4: $-\frac{1}{8\pi r}\, e^{ikr}$

As for the first integral in (1-16) we can also define it as performed along L_1, L_2, L_3, or L_4, but the integrand will decrease exponentially only when p is given a positive imaginary part so that we shall close the contour by a semicircle C′ in the upper half-plane as indicated in Fig. 1-2 (when we have considered the case of path L_4). We thus get for the first term in (1-16),

integrated along L_1: 0

integrated along L_2: $-\frac{1}{8\pi r}\left[e^{-ikr} + e^{ikr}\right]$

integrated along L_3: $-\frac{1}{8\pi r}\, e^{-ikr}$

integrated along L_4: $-\frac{1}{8\pi r}\, e^{ikr}$

We see now that there is only one way of defining G(r) in order that it behaves as a pure outgoing wave for large values of r, and this is to write, in place of (1-15),

$$G(r) = \frac{1}{4\pi^2} \int_{L_4} \frac{\sin pr}{r} \, \frac{p\, dp}{k^2 - p^2} \tag{1-17}$$

G(r) will then be given by the sum of the two terms written in (1-16), giving

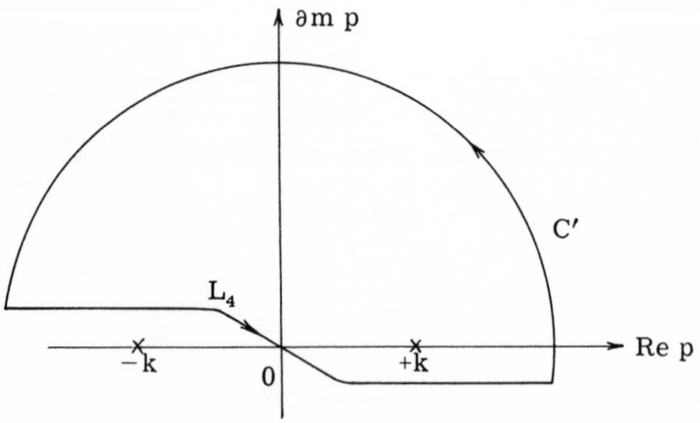

Figure 1-2

$$G(r) = \frac{1}{4\pi} \frac{e^{ikr}}{r} \tag{1-18}$$

Let us now see the physical meaning of (1-17) and (1-18). The definition (1-17) of G(r) has been derived from the not-well-defined expression (2-15) by pushing the integration contour around the two poles $\pm k$. We could as well have pushed the pole $p = -k$ below the real axis and the pole $p = +k$ above the real axis, keeping that real axis as the integration path. That would mean taking for the poles $p = \pm(k + i\varepsilon)$, i.e., just adding an infinitesimal positive imaginary part $i\varepsilon$ to k. Then

$$G(r) = \frac{1}{(2\pi)^3} \int e^{i\mathbf{p}\cdot\mathbf{x}} \frac{d^3p}{(k + i\varepsilon)^2 - \mathbf{p}^2} \tag{1-19}$$

Adding such an $i\varepsilon$ to k in (1-18) only makes G(r) decrease as $e^{-\varepsilon r}$, when r is large and will not affect essentially the properties of G(r) when it multiplies a wave function, while, should we have replaced k by $k - i\varepsilon$, we should have got an exploding factor $e^{\varepsilon r}$, which, when multiplying a wave function, would have given something without physical meaning, i.e., a new wave function corresponding to an exponentially increasing probability density of particles at an infinite distance.

As for the explicit form (1-18) of G(r) we can make a few comments to clarify its structure:

1. Its phase is given by e^{ikr}, which only ensures that the free particles diverge after scattering as spherical waves with a momentum of magnitude k.

2. For large values of r, the factor r^{-1} ensures that the number of particles per unit time emerging through a sphere of radius r does not depend on that radius, i.e., the conservation of particles.

3. For small values of r, G(r) behaves as $1/4\pi r$. In fact, recalling that G(r) was defined as $(\nabla^2 + k^2)^{-1}$, we must have

$$(\nabla^2 + k^2)G(\mathbf{x}) = \delta(\mathbf{x}) \tag{1-20}$$

since the produce of $\nabla^2 + k^2$ by $G(x - y)$ must be the identity operator, or $\delta(x - y)$, so that, for $k^2 = 0$, we must find that $G(\mathbf{x})$ tends to the potential created by a unit electrostatic charge at the origin, i.e., $-1/4\pi r$, since then (1-20) becomes the Poisson equation for that potential

$$\nabla^2 V(\mathbf{x}) = \delta(\mathbf{x})$$

To conclude, we shall write the formal relation (1-8) as an explicit integral relation for the wave function; replacing $(\nabla^2 + k^2)^{-1}$ by its explicit form (1-18) and using (1-2) we have

$$\Psi(\mathbf{x}) = e^{i\mathbf{k}\cdot\mathbf{x}} - \frac{1}{4\pi}\int \frac{e^{ik|\mathbf{x}-\mathbf{y}|}}{|\mathbf{x}-\mathbf{y}|} V(\mathbf{y})\Psi(\mathbf{y})\, d^3y \qquad (1\text{-}21)$$

That integral equation may look at first sight more complicated than the Schrödinger equation, but its enormous advantage is that it takes automatically into account the boundary conditions of the scattering problems.

1-3 THE BORN SERIES EXPANSION

We shall now use (1-21) to get an explicit expression of the wave function as a series (which is known as the Born series) and to follow more closely how scattering proceeds in detail. To do so, it is not necessary to use (1-21) in its completely explicit form, but we shall rather use the form (1-8) as

$$\Psi = \varphi_i + \frac{1}{\nabla^2 + k^2} V\Psi \qquad (1\text{-}22)$$

where we have written φ_i for the incident plane wave $e^{i\mathbf{k}\cdot\mathbf{x}}$. In that relation, Ψ may be replaced in the right-hand member by its expression as given by the whole equation (1-22), giving an integrated form of (1-22),

$$\Psi = \varphi_i + \frac{1}{\nabla^2 + k^2} V\varphi_i + \frac{1}{\nabla^2 + k^2} V \frac{1}{\nabla^2 + k^2} V\Psi$$

We may again replace Ψ in the right-hand member by its expression (1-22), and so on, so that we get a series expansion for Ψ:

$$\Psi = \varphi_i + \frac{1}{\nabla^2 + k^2} V\varphi_i + \frac{1}{\nabla^2 + k^2} V \frac{1}{\nabla^2 + k^2} V\varphi_i + \cdots \qquad (1\text{-}23)$$

Let us give a physical picture of that relation. We may say: The total wave function consists of a series of terms describing the detailed history of the scattering. There is first a term φ_i, which is, as we have seen, both the incident plane wave and the outgoing plane wave corresponding to particles which have not suffered scattering. Then there are particles which interact once with the potential: The initial wave φ is multiplied by the potential V at the point where interaction of the particle and the scattering takes place and an outgoing spherical wave results which is represented in our expression by the term $(\nabla^2 + k^2)^{-1}$. We shall picture that interaction by drawing a line for the ingoing particle and one for the outgoing particle with a vertex where the action of potential takes place (Fig. 1-3). Such a graph

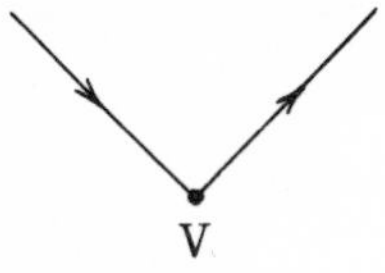

Figure 1-3

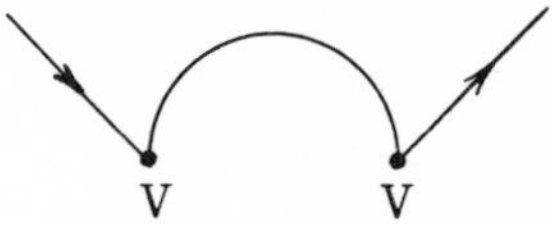

Figure 1-4

corresponds to the second term in (1-23). Now, the outgoing particle may scatter again at another position, the corresponding modification of the wave function, interaction, and radiation being again represented by a factor $(\nabla^2 + k^2)^{-1}V$. We thus associate the third term in (1-23) with the graph of Fig. 1-4, and so on.

The Born series may consequently be considered as a description of the total scattering as a multiple scattering by the individual points where interaction takes place. Obviously, such a description will be most useful when multiple scattering is smallest, i.e., when the potential is small. In particular, the existence and properties of bound states as well as resonances are not conveniently described by Born series. As concerns resonances, this may be understood as follows: A resonance in scattering may be identified with a metastable bound state of the scattered particle and the target, as has been emphasized in the compound nucleus model by N. Bohr. Such a metastable state has to live much longer than the interaction time, i.e., the interval of time during which the particle crosses the target. But in order that the particle be trapped such a long time, it is necessary that, during the time it would need to cross the target, it suffers many individual scatterings. A resonance corresponds, then, precisely to the conditions where the successive terms of (1-23) do not decrease, and for a bound state it is, of course, even worse. From the mathematical viewpoint, it may be shown that it is precisely the existence of bound states and resonances which limits the convergence of the Born series expression. We shall examine this point in more detail in Sec. 3-5.

1-4 CALCULATION OF THE SCATTERING AMPLITUDE

As we have seen, the scattering amplitude is defined by the asymptotic form of the wave function for large values of $|\mathbf{x}|$:

$$\Psi(\mathbf{x}) \sim e^{i\mathbf{k}\cdot\mathbf{x}} + f(\theta)\,\frac{e^{ikr}}{r} \tag{1-24}$$

The integral equation (1-21) for $\Psi(\mathbf{x})$ makes explicitly the separation of the incident plane wave $e^{i\mathbf{k}\cdot\mathbf{x}}$, so that it is natural to look for the asymptotic form of the second term of (1-21) in order to get an explicit expression of the scattering amplitude. We shall thus look for the properties of the integral

$$\int \frac{e^{ik|\mathbf{x}-\mathbf{y}|}}{|\mathbf{x}-\mathbf{y}|} V(\mathbf{y})\Psi(\mathbf{y})\, d^3y$$

If the interaction is localized [or if $V(\mathbf{y})$ decreases sufficiently rapidly when $|\mathbf{y}|$ becomes large], we may consider that the domain of integration on $\mathbf{y}$ is finite, so that we can neglect $\mathbf{y}$ compared to $\mathbf{x}$ in the denominator $|\mathbf{x}-\mathbf{y}|$. On the other hand, the phase factor $e^{ik(\mathbf{x}-\mathbf{y})}$ will depend sensitively on $\mathbf{y}$, no matter how large $|\mathbf{x}|$ is. We shall thus extract its main dependence on $\mathbf{x}$ by writing

$$|\mathbf{x}-\mathbf{y}| = [(\mathbf{x}-\mathbf{y})^2]^{1/2} = [\mathbf{x}^2 - 2\mathbf{x}\cdot\mathbf{y} + \mathbf{y}^2]^{1/2}$$

$$= |\mathbf{x}| \left[1 - \frac{2\mathbf{x}\cdot\mathbf{y}}{|\mathbf{x}|^2} + \frac{\mathbf{y}^2}{|\mathbf{x}|^2}\right]^{1/2}$$

For $\mathbf{x}$ large enough, the last term y^2/x^2 is negligible, so that

$$|\mathbf{x}-\mathbf{y}| \simeq |\mathbf{x}| \left[1 - \frac{2\mathbf{x}\cdot\mathbf{y}}{|\mathbf{x}|^2}\right]^{1/2} \simeq |\mathbf{x}| - \frac{\mathbf{x}\cdot\mathbf{y}}{|\mathbf{x}|}$$

Let us now introduce a new notation: when making the observation of the scattered particle at a point $\mathbf{x}$ which is at a large distance from the target, we shall call $\mathbf{k}' = k(\mathbf{x}/|\mathbf{x}|)$ the corresponding momentum of the particle, the absolute value of which is obviously k. Writing $|\mathbf{x}| = r$, we have thus got

$$e^{ik|\mathbf{x}-\mathbf{y}|} \simeq e^{ikr - \mathbf{k}'\cdot\mathbf{y}}$$

or

$$\Psi(\mathbf{x}) \simeq e^{i\mathbf{k}\cdot\mathbf{x}} - \frac{1}{4\pi}\frac{e^{ikr}}{r} \int e^{-i\mathbf{k}'\cdot\mathbf{y}}\, V(y)\Psi(\mathbf{y})\, d^3y \qquad (1\text{-}25)$$

For the sake of clarity, we shall write the scattering amplitude $f(\mathbf{k}\cdot\mathbf{k}')$ in place of $f(\theta)$, since θ is nothing but the angle between the initial momentum $\mathbf{k}$ and the final momentum $\mathbf{k}'$. Then comparing (1-24) and (1-25), we obtain the following explicit expression for the scattering amplitude:

$$f(\mathbf{k}\cdot\mathbf{k}') = -\frac{1}{4\pi} \int e^{-i\mathbf{k}'\cdot\mathbf{y}}\, V(y)\Psi(\mathbf{y})\, d^3y \qquad (1\text{-}26)$$

Equation (1-26) is extremely useful in practice in order to derive the mathematical properties of the scattering amplitude. However, as we are not interested in a rigorous analysis, we shall not need it in precisely that form. We shall need rather a series expansion for $f(\mathbf{k}\cdot\mathbf{k}')$ which may be derived as a consequence of the Born series (1-23) and of (1-26). To obtain it, note that (1-26) means that we can define the scattering amplitude as a scalar product,

$$f_{fi} = -\frac{1}{4\pi}\left(\varphi_f^*, V\Psi\right) \tag{1-27}$$

where φ_f is written for the plane wave $e^{i\mathbf{k}'\cdot\mathbf{y}}$ of an observed final state. Then, multiplying the Born series (1-23) on the left by V and taking its scalar product by φ_f, we get

$$-4\pi f_{fi} = \left(\varphi_f^*, V\varphi_i\right) + \left(\varphi_f^*, V\frac{1}{\nabla^2 + k^2}V\varphi_i\right) + \left(\varphi_f^*, V\frac{1}{\nabla^2 + k^2}V\frac{1}{\nabla^2 + k^2}\varphi_i\right) + \cdots \tag{1-28}$$

That expression of f will be used below to derive the main mathematical properties of the scattering amplitude. Its physical content is obviously the same as that of the Born series for Ψ, and it may be given the same graphical interpretation. We can write (1-28) in more detail, using Dirac's notation and expanding the operator $1/(\nabla^2 + k^2)$ according to its eigenvectors and eigenvalues:

$$\frac{1}{\nabla^2 + k^2} = \sum_{\mathbf{p}} |\mathbf{p}\rangle \frac{1}{k^2 - \mathbf{p}^2}\langle\mathbf{p}|$$

$$= \frac{1}{(2\pi)^3}\int |\mathbf{p}\rangle \frac{d^3p}{k^2 - \mathbf{p}^2}\langle\mathbf{p}|$$

This integral is defined only if we add that it has to be considered as a limit when k becomes real after having a small positive imaginary part; see (1-19). We thus write

$$-4\pi f(\mathbf{k}',\mathbf{k}) = \langle k'|V|k\rangle + \frac{1}{(2\pi)^3}\int \langle k'|V|p\rangle \frac{d^3p}{(k+i\varepsilon)^2 - \mathbf{p}^2} \times \langle p|V|k\rangle + \frac{1}{(2\pi)^6}\int \langle k'|V|p_1\rangle \frac{d^3p_1}{(k+i\varepsilon)^2 - \mathbf{p}_1^2} \times \langle p_1|V|p_2\rangle \frac{d^3p_2}{(k+i\varepsilon)^2 - \mathbf{p}_2^2}\langle p_2|V|k\rangle + \cdots \tag{1-29}$$

We have, of course, replaced the φ_i and φ_f by the ket vectors $|k\rangle$ and $|k'\rangle$ of the incoming and outgoing particles. We recall also that

$$\langle p | V | p' \rangle = \int e^{+i\mathbf{p}\cdot\mathbf{x} - i\mathbf{p}'\cdot\mathbf{x}} V(\mathbf{x})\, d\mathbf{x} \tag{1-30}$$

2

PROPERTIES OF PARTIAL WAVES

We have seen in Chapter 1 how it was possible to solve the scattering problem by using the Born series solution which is given by (1-28). Unfortunately, this series is useless when we want to study the more interesting features of scattering, namely, the resonances and how the existence of bound states reflects itself on the scattering amplitude. As we have already said, it is precisely the existence of bound states and resonances which precludes the convergence of the Born series.

In the very general case where the potential is spherically symmetric, there is much to be gained in separating the angular variables through a spherical harmonics expansion. That will lead us actually to a one-dimensional form of the Schrödinger equation whose solutions have asymptotic properties for large values of r which are more transparent than in the case of the three-dimensional Schrödinger equation. Since the study of those properties is precisely the subject matter of the scattering theory, we shall thus get much more precise information, and, in particular, we shall be able to find what is the precise meaning of a resonance and how bound states may appear as characteristics of a general scattering theory.

2-1 SEPARATION OF THE SCHRÖDINGER EQUATION IN PARTIAL WAVES

We shall thus now begin to study the scattering from a spherically symmetric potential. More precisely we shall restrict ourselves to a particular class of interactions which will be in fact the type of potentials that we expect to appear between elementary particles. It is well known that the first elementary-particle potential introduced theoretically is the function $e^{-\mu r}/r$ introduced by Yukawa in 1937 to represent nucleon-nucleon interaction in a first approximation. This potential has very "smooth" properties: It decreases exponentially for large values of r, so that we can say that it acts essentially at a distance of a few $r_0 = 1/\mu$. This length r_0 is called the *range* of the potential. For small values of r, the potential behaves as r^{-1}, which in fact does not affect strongly the solution. Actually we know (and we shall recall in a few pages) that the effective potential in a state of definite angular momentum is $V(r) + [\ell(\ell + 1)/r^2]$ so that the singularity at the origin of a Yukawa potential, which is proportional to $1/r$, will be completely negligible as compared to the centrifugal barrier potential, which behaves as $1/r^2$.

It is possible to have a more general class of potentials having essentially the same smooth properties by taking

$$V(r) = A_1 \frac{e^{-\mu_1 r}}{r} + A_2 \frac{e^{-\mu_2 r}}{r} + \cdots + \int_{\mu_0}^{\infty} B(\mu') \frac{e^{-\mu' r}}{r} \, d\mu'$$

Here V(r) is a discrete sum of Yukawa potentials and of an integral of potentials whose largest range is $1/\mu_0$. We shall say that V(r) is a superposition of Yukawa potentials. We shall see in the following chapters that there are good reasons to believe that the potentials between elementary particles, as far as we can speak actually of such potentials, are certainly of that form.

Let us now go to the separation of the angular variables in scattering. We assume that the reader is already familiar with the elementary quantum-mechanical theory of the angular momentum. Howevery, we recall here the main results for the sake of completeness and to define the notation.

Let us choose the z axis in the direction of the incoming beam (Chapter 1). The wave function $\Psi(\mathbf{x})$ depends only upon the radial coordinate $r = |\mathbf{x}|$, and upon the angle θ between the z axis and $\mathbf{x}$ but not upon the third polar coordinate φ. This already achieves in a simple way the elimination of one variable. To eliminate the second variable θ, we separate $\Psi(\mathbf{x})$ according to the eigenvalues of the angular-momentum squared, $\mathbf{L}^2 = \ell(\ell + 1)$, by writing

$$\Psi(\mathbf{x}) = \sum_{\ell=0}^{\infty} \frac{y_\ell(r)}{r} P_\ell(\cos\theta) \tag{2-1}$$

where $P_\ell(\cos\theta)$ is the usual Legendre polynomial of degree ℓ. The three-dimensional Schrödinger equation then decomposes into a set of one-dimensional equations involving separately each one of the $y_\ell(r)$:

$$\frac{d^2 y_\ell(r)}{dr^2} + \left[k^2 - V(r) - \frac{\ell(\ell + 1)}{r^2}\right] y_\ell(r) = 0 \qquad (2\text{-}2)$$

The last term in the bracket is the familiar centrifugal barrier term. The presence of a coefficient $1/r$ in the right-hand side of (2-1) implies that $y_\ell(r)$ has to go to zero at the origin $r = 0$. Otherwise, $\Psi(\mathbf{x})$ would have a singularity at $\mathbf{x} = 0$, which would render its physical interpretation impossible.

The properties of the partial wave functions $y_\ell(r)$ for large values of r may be easily deduced from (2-2). When r is large enough, we can neglect the exponentially decreasing $V(r)$ and $\ell(\ell + 1)/r^2$ as compared with the constant k^2, so that the radial Schrödinger equation (2-2) takes the simple form

$$\frac{d^2 y_\ell}{dr^2} + k^2 y_\ell(r) = 0$$

The solution of that equation is proportional to $\sin(kr + \alpha_\ell)$, where α_ℓ is any fixed phase. We shall choose to write

$$y_\ell(r) \underset{r\to\infty}{\sim} C_\ell \sin\left(kr - \frac{\ell\pi}{2} + \delta_\ell\right) \qquad (2\text{-}3)$$

where we have separated the phase $-\ell\pi/2$ which is introduced by the centrifugal when there is no potential. Actually, it may be shown that the solution of the equation

$$\frac{d^2 y_\ell}{dr^2} + \left[k^2 - \frac{\ell(\ell + 1)}{r^2}\right] y_\ell(r) = 0$$

is given by (2-3), with $\delta_\ell = 0$. We can thus say that the so-called phase shift δ_ℓ is completely determined by the potential $V(r)$, and δ_ℓ vanishes together with $V(r)$.

It will be useful to relate the asymptotic form of the radial wave function (2-3) to the asymptotic form of the total wave function (1-5) in order to get relations between the scattering amplitude and the phase shifts. To do so, we shall systematically write all the interesting quantities as superpositions of incoming spherical wave functions which behave like e^{-ikr}/r for r large and outgoing waves which behave like e^{ikr}/r. Equation (2-3) will then appear as

$$y_\ell(r) \underset{r\to\infty}{\sim} \frac{G_\ell}{2i} \left(e^{ikr - i\ell\pi/2 + i\delta_\ell} - e^{-ikr + i\ell\pi/2 - i\delta_\ell}\right) \qquad (2\text{-}4)$$

and we shall use for the asymptotic behavior of the plane wave,

$$e^{ikz} = \sum_{\ell=0}^{\infty} \frac{Y_\ell(r)}{r} P_\ell(\cos\theta) \tag{2-5}$$

$$Y_\ell(r) = (2\ell + 1) r i^\ell j_\ell(kr)$$

$$\underset{r\to\infty}{\sim} \frac{2\ell+1}{2ki}\left(e^{ikr} - e^{-ikr+i\ell\pi}\right) \tag{2-6}$$

As the scattering process creates only outgoing waves, all the incoming spherical wave part of y_ℓ must pertain to e^{ikz}, so that we must identify the second term of (2-4) with the corresponding term of (2-6). That fixes the value of the coefficient G_ℓ as

$$G_\ell = \frac{2\ell+1}{k} e^{i\delta_\ell + i\ell\pi/2} \tag{2-7}$$

so that, putting (2-7) into (2-4), we get a more precise form of the partial-wave asymptotic behavior:

$$y_\ell(r) = \frac{2\ell+1}{2ki}\left(e^{ikr+2i\delta_\ell} - e^{-ikr+i\ell\pi}\right) \tag{2-8}$$

We can now isolate the contribution of the plane wave e^{ikz} to the partial wave $y_\ell(r)$ by writing

$$y_\ell(r) = Y_\ell(r) + y_\ell^{sc}(r) \tag{2-9}$$

so that the scattered partial wave $y_\ell^{sc}(r)$ will just be the contribution of the scattered wave function $f(\theta)\, e^{ikr}/r$ to the angular momentum ℓ. It is easy to relate it to the phase shift, since

$$y_\ell^{sc}(r) = y_\ell(r) - Y_\ell(r)$$

$$= \frac{2\ell+1}{2ki} e^{ikr}\left(e^{2i\delta_\ell} - 1\right)$$

$$= \frac{2\ell+1}{k} e^{i\delta_\ell} \sin\delta_\ell \, e^{ikr} \tag{2-10}$$

We check that it is purely outgoing, as it should be. It is very easy now to compute the scattering amplitude, by summing up the series (2-1).

$$\Psi(\mathbf{x}) = \sum_{\ell=0}^{\infty} \frac{y_\ell(r)}{r} P_\ell(\cos\theta)$$

$$= \sum_{\ell=0}^{\infty} \frac{Y_\ell(r)}{r} P_\ell(\cos\theta) + \sum_{\ell=0}^{\infty} \frac{y_\ell^{sc}(r)}{r} P_\ell(\cos\theta)$$

The first series on the right-hand side reconstitutes the incident plane wave, and the second term is a sum of purely outgoing waves, and we find (1-5),

$$\Psi(\mathbf{x}) \underset{r\to\infty}{\approx} e^{ikz} + \frac{e^{ikr}}{r} f(k^2, \cos\theta) \qquad (1\text{-}5)$$

with

$$\boxed{f(k^2, \cos\theta) = \sum_{\ell=0}^{\infty} \frac{2\ell + 1}{k} e^{i\delta_\ell} \sin\delta_\ell \, P_\ell(\cos\theta)} \qquad (2\text{-}11)$$

This is a basic equation which we shall use quite often. By analogy with the name of *scattering amplitude* for $f(k^2, \cos\theta)$, we shall call *partial-wave amplitude* the quantity

$$a_\ell(k^2) = \frac{1}{k} e^{i\delta_\ell} \sin\delta_\ell \qquad (2\text{-}12)$$

which appears in the series (2-11).

Another very useful formula is the inverse formula, which allows us to compute the partial-wave amplitude from the scattering amplitude:

$$a_\ell(k^2) = \tfrac{1}{2} \int_{-1}^{+1} P_\ell(\cos\theta) f(k^2, \cos\theta) \, d\cos\theta \qquad (2\text{-}13)$$

which is easily checked from (2-11) by using the well-known formula (orthogonality relation of the Legendre polynomials)

$$\frac{2\ell + 1}{2} \int_{-1}^{+1} P_\ell(x) P_m(x) \, dx = \delta_{\ell m} = \begin{cases} 1 & \ell = m \\ 0 & \ell \neq m \end{cases}$$

2-2 STUDY OF THE RADIAL EQUATION

Now that all kinematical features implied by angular momentum conservation have been taken care of, we are left with the essential dynamical problem of relating the phase shift δ_ℓ to the potential $V(r)$.

In mathematical terms the problem appears as follows: to find a solution of the radial Schrödinger equation (2-2), which vanishes at the origin (in order to be physically interpretable), and comparing its asymptotic form with formula (2-8) to find the phase shift δ_ℓ. The presence of the centrifugal term, however, makes the equation (2-2) fairly singular at the origin, and we have to investigate carefully what is the behavior of the solutions in the neighborhood of $r = 0$. For very small r, we may neglect the contributions of k^2 and of $V(r)$ in (2-2) and the equation then becomes

$$\frac{d^2 y_\ell(r)}{dr^2} - \frac{\ell(\ell+1)}{r^2} y_\ell(r) = 0$$

The two independent solutions of this equation are

$$y_\ell(r) = r^{\ell+1} \qquad \text{and} \qquad y_\ell(r) = r^{-\ell}$$

The second leads to infinite values of $y_\ell(0)$ and must be rejected. As for the first one, it depends only upon a normalization factor as expressed in (2-3). Obviously, the definition of the phase shift δ_ℓ does not depend on this normalization factor. We chose it as G_ℓ given by (2-7) when we wanted to compare the three-dimensional treatment of scattering with the one-dimensional form. However, it will be more convenient now to use another choice.

To define it we must give the value of the wave function at some place. The easiest choice is clearly one where the wave function depends least upon the potential and the value of k^2, that is, the origin. We define then a new normalization (which actually ensures also the requirement of vanishing at the origin) by considering the particular solution $u_\ell(k^2,r)$ of (2-2) such that

$$\frac{u_\ell(k^2,r)}{r^{\ell+1}} \to 1 \qquad \text{as } r \to 0 \tag{2-14}$$

The asymptotic form of $u_\ell(r)$ is still given by (2-4), up to a constant factor. We shall express it in terms of incoming and outgoing waves as

$$u_\ell(k^2,r) \underset{r\to\infty}{\sim} \varphi^-(\ell,k^2)\, e^{ikr} + \varphi^+(\ell,k^2)\, e^{-ikr} \tag{2-15}$$

The coefficients φ^+ and φ^-, which are defined by (2-15), are called Jost's functions. As $u_\ell(r)$ is real, φ^+ and φ^- are complex conjugate of each other. By comparing with (2-8), for example, we can deduce immediately:

$$e^{2i\delta_\ell} = S(\ell,k^2) = (-1)^{\ell+1} \frac{\varphi^-(\ell,k^2)}{\varphi^+(\ell,k^2)} \tag{2-16}$$

so that the problem of determining the phase shifts is now replaced by that of determining one of the Jost functions.

2-3 ANALYTIC PROPERTIES OF THE PARTIAL-WAVE AMPLITUDE AS A FUNCTION OF k^2

The normalization we have used to define u_ℓ is very useful, as we see that, in general, u_ℓ will vary very smoothly if we vary any of the parameters in (2-2). The reason is that in the immediate neighborhood of $r = 0$, $u_\ell(k^2,r)$ does not vary appreciably if we modify k^2, for example. As $\ell(\ell + 1)/r^2$ decreases, the variation of $u_\ell(k^2,r)$ with k^2 will be more and more important with increasing r, but it sets in so gradually that one does not expect any anomaly for any given r. Such an analysis of solutions of differential equation had already been made by Poincaré, and he indeed proved that, under suitable conditions, the solutions of a differential equation are so smooth that they are analytic functions of the parameters in the equation. With a slight extension, this theorem is also true in our case, so that it may be proved that $u_\ell(k^2,r)$ is in fact an analytic function of k^2. We may then ask first whether this implies conditions on the phase shift, and second whether these conditions have any physical implications. There for the first time we have to go outside of the physical region. (The reader is supposed to be at least a little familiar with the concept of analytic functions, and to know how interesting it is to consider an analytic function not only for real values of the variable, here k^2, but also for complex values.)

In fact, we shall now proceed as follows: We shall consider the radial Schrödinger equation

$$\frac{d^2u_\ell}{dr^2} + \left[k^2 - V(r) - \frac{\ell(\ell + 1)}{r^2}\right] u_\ell(r) = 0$$

for any real or complex values of the parameter k^2. We shall only consider the solution of that equation such that $u_\ell r^{-\ell-1}$ tends to 1 when r tends to zero, which defines completely the solution. Then we shall define the Jost's functions $\varphi^\pm(\ell,k^2)$ by studying the asymptotic behavior of $u_\ell(r)$ for large values of r [(2-15)], and we shall define the phase shifts $\delta_\ell(k^2)$ through (2-16) as the quotient of the two Jost's functions. That will allow us to get much more insight in the way this phase shift can vary as a function of k^2.

After having solved that mathematical problem, it will be possible to obtain information about the *physical* values of $\delta_\ell(k^2)$ just by restricting k^2 to be real and positive.

The only nonsimple question in that mathematical problem is to see if we can actually define the Jost's functions. We shall actually see that there are two sets of values of k^2 for which this is nontrivial, and this problem will lead us to find the singularities of $\varphi^\pm(\ell,k^2)$.

2-4 THE LEFT-HAND CUT

When we want to consider the asymptotic properties of $u_\ell(r)$ and be sure that it behaves as a sum of two terms proportional to $e^{\pm ikr}$, it is necessary to neglect $V(r)u_\ell(r)$ and $\ell(\ell + 1)u_\ell(r)/r^2$ as compared with the other terms. If that is possible, we are then sure that (2-15) may be written correctly and that the Jost's functions are well defined.

$$u_\ell(k^2,r) \underset{r\to\infty}{\sim} \varphi^-(\ell,k^2)\, e^{ikr} + \varphi^+(\ell,k^2)\, e^{-ikr} \tag{2-15}$$

It is now necessary to make precise what we mean by k when k^2 is complex: We shall choose to define it as being the root of $\sqrt{k^2}$ with a positive imaginary part (that choice will permit a simple passage to the physical case as suggested by the $k + i\varepsilon$ which we have found in the definition of the Green's function in Chapter 1).

There is a case where analyticity of the wave function $u_\ell(k^2,r)$ as a function of k^2 does not imply analyticity for the functions $\varphi^\pm(\ell,k^2)$, because the asymptotic formula (2-15) does not apply. When k^2 becomes real and negative, the first exponential in (2-15) becomes purely damped, $e^{ikr} = e^{-|k|r}$, and the second one purely explosive, $e^{-ikr} = e^{+|k|r}$.

As the Yukawa-type potentials which we are considering have an exponential character in r (of the type $e^{-\mu r}/r$), the separation of the first term of (2-15) is justified if only the damped exponential e^{ikr} does not decrease too fast. Actually, if $|k|$ is bigger than $\mu/2$ for the case of a single Yukawa potential $g^2\, e^{-\mu r}/r$, it would be nonsense to neglect the potential term $e^{-\mu r}$ when it multiplies the explosive part $e^{|kr|}$ of $u_\ell(r)$ and gives terms in the equation proportional to $e^{(|k|-\mu)r}$ and to keep the damped term $e^{-|k|r}$ in $u_\ell(r)$.

We must then consider that (2-15) has no more sense when k^2 is real and less than $-\mu^2/4$. Consequently, the Jost's functions is not well defined for these values, and it is impossible to infer analyticity for them from the analyticity of $u_\ell(k^2,r)$. In fact, it may be proved that there is a singularity on the negative real k^2 axis at $k^2 = -\mu^2/4$ whose nature is clearly dependent upon the potential.

If we have more generally a superposition of Yukawa potentials, we shall get a line of potential-dependent singularities on the negative real k^2 axis, starting at $k^2 = -\mu_0^2/4$, where μ_0 is the smallest of the inverse ranges. We shall therefore always avoid this part of the k^2 plane, considering it as cut from $-\mu_0^2/4$ to $-\infty$.

2-5 THE RIGHT-HAND CUT

Another case where the asymptotic form (2-15) is not valid is when k^2 is equal to zero, for then we can no longer neglect $V(r) + \ell(\ell+1)/r^2$ as compared to k^2.

If we take any very large value R of r, there is a small enough value $k^2 = \ell(\ell+1)/R^2$, below which the asymptotic form is not valid for $r < R$. In other words, at zero energy the centrifugal barrier (or the potential barrier, if $\ell = 0$) is always stronger than the vanishing kinetic energy of the incident particle, and therefore the asymptotic behavior of the wave function is entirely different from that given by (2-15).

We thus expect that the Jost's functions have a singularity around $k^2 = 0$. This is in fact well known from elementary quantum mechanics, where it is shown that the phase shifts $\delta_\ell(k^2)$, for small physical values of k^2, behave as $k^{2\ell+1}$; that is, they are not analytic functions of k^2 but of k. It may be shown that the same results are valid for the Jost functions and that they are also analytic as functions of k. Let us now see in more detail what this change of variable from k^2 to k implies.

It is in fact simpler to start from k as a variable. In that case, we shall write $\varphi(\ell,k)$ for the Jost's function $\varphi^-(\ell,k^2)$. As a function of k, it has no singularity at the origin. As it is not well defined for k^2 negative between $-\mu_0^2/4$ and $-\infty$, it has *a priori* two corresponding cuts as a function of k from $k = i\mu_0/2$ to $+i\infty$ and from $k = -i\mu_0/2$ to $-i\infty$. [It may be shown, in fact, that the upper cut does not exist as it is $\varphi^+(\ell,k^2)$ and not $\varphi^-(\ell,k^2)$, which is not well defined for k imaginary, $\text{Im}\, k > \mu_0/2$.]

There is a remarkable symmetry of the Jost functions with respect to the exchange between k and $-k$. This operation does not in fact modify the radial Schrödinger equation, which depends only on k^2, nor the boundary condition for $u_\ell(k^2,r)$ at the origin, since that condition does not contain k^2. Therefore, $u_\ell(k^2 r)$ is not changed by the exchange. However, in (2-15) the two terms $e^{\pm ikr}$ are exchanged, so that one has

$$\varphi^+(\ell,k) = \varphi^-(\ell,-k) \tag{2-17}$$

If we want to visualize these functions as functions of k^2, it will be convenient to view the k^2 plane as made up of two superposed planes, or sheets, which correspond to the two possible choices of k. To specify these choices, we shall say that if $\text{Im } k > 0$, we are on the *physical sheet*, and if $\text{Im } k < 0$, we choose the *unphysical sheet*. These two sheets have a common boundary, which is $\text{Im } k = 0$, or k real or else k^2 real and positive. But they connect in a cross-wise fashion, that is, A: $k^2 + i\varepsilon$ (physical sheet) is near B: $k^2 - i\varepsilon$ (unphysical sheet), while C: $k^2 - i\varepsilon$ (physical sheet) has to be considered far from both A and B, as $k_C \sim -k_A \sim -k_B$. It is perhaps convenient to picture the two sheets as in Fig. 2-1, where we have drawn the shortest paths between A and B or C.

A set of sheets above a complex plane is called a Riemann surface. It is completely defined once the common boundaries of the sheets (here positive real k^2) and the connections across them are given. A place like the origin $k^2 = 0$ here, which is common to several sheets, is called a *branch point*.

This study completes the analysis of the singularity of $\varphi^{\pm}(\ell,k)$ at $k^2 = 0$: It is simply a branch point of order two, that is, common to only two sheets. It is a kinematical singularity, in the sense that its nature and location do not depend upon the potential. (Remember that its origin was the centrifugal barrier.) Furthermore, it is of a rather trivial nature, as may be seen from (2-17), as the passage from one sheet to the other (changing k into $-k$) simply exchanges φ^+ and φ^-, that is, changes

$$e^{2i\delta} = S(\ell,k) = (-1)^{\ell+1} \frac{\varphi^-(\ell,k^2)}{\varphi^+(\ell,k^2)}$$

into its inverse.

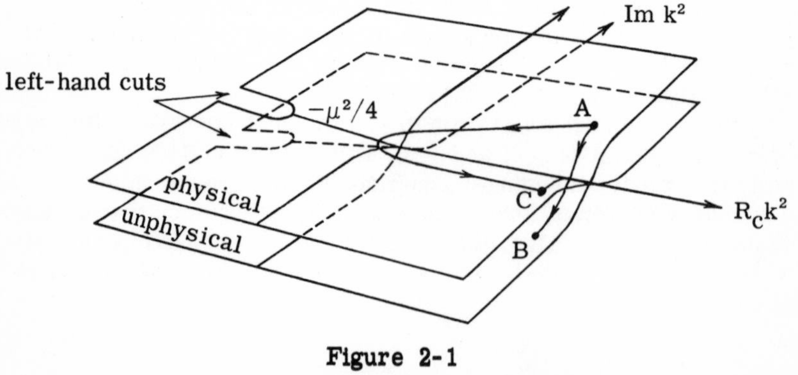

Figure 2-1

2-6 ANALYTIC PROPERTIES OF THE PARTIAL-WAVE AMPLITUDE

Consider now the partial-wave amplitude itself, $a_\ell(k^2)$,

$$a_\ell(k^2) = \frac{e^{i\delta_\ell} \sin \delta_\ell}{k} = \frac{1}{2ik}\left(e^{2i\delta_\ell} - 1\right)$$

It may be easily expressed in terms of the Jost functions as

$$a_\ell(k^2) = \frac{1}{2ik}\left[(-1)^{\ell+1} \frac{\varphi^-(\ell,k^2)}{\varphi^+(\ell,k^2)} - 1\right]$$

and it will be an analytic function of k^2 with the same singularities as the Jost functions, i.e., a left-hand cut and a physical cut in k^2. Furthermore, $a_\ell(k^2)$ may get poles where $\varphi^+(\ell,k^2)$ is zero.

Later on we shall consider in more detail the poles of the partial-wave amplitude. For the time being, we shall first try to clarify the properties of $a_\ell(k^2)$ as a function of k or, if preferred, as a function of k^2 on the two physical and unphysical sheets.

This is most easily done by first considering the corresponding properties of the function $S(\ell,k^2)$. Consider again the two points B and C of the Riemann surface, which are one above the other and correspond to the same value of k^2. Our problem will be to specify $S(\ell,k^2)$ on B. To make a clearcut distinction, we shall keep the notation $S(\ell,k^2)$ for k^2 in the physical sheet and we shall write $S^I(\ell,k^2)$ for k^2 in the unphysical sheet. The two points B and C correspond to opposite values of k, which gives immediately the relation between S and S^I.

$$S^I(\ell,k^2) = (-1)^{\ell+1} \frac{\varphi^-(\ell,-k)}{\varphi^+(\ell,k)}$$

$$= (-1)^{\ell+1} \frac{\varphi^+(\ell,k)}{\varphi^-(\ell,-k)} = \frac{1}{S(\ell,k^2)} \qquad (2\text{-}18)$$

[the second equality follows from (2-17)]. This equality thereby defines the values taken by the analytic continuation of $a_\ell(k^2)$; let it be $a_\ell^I(k^2)$:

$$1 - 2kia_\ell^I(k^2) = \frac{1}{1 + 2kia_\ell(k^2)}$$

or

$$a_\ell^I(k^2) = \frac{a_\ell(k^2)}{1 + 2kia_\ell(k^2)} \qquad (2\text{-}19)$$

(We have used the fact that the analytic continuation of k into the unphysical sheet is a function $k^I = -k$.)

We can summarize the information expressed by (2-19) by saying that everything that happens in the unphysical sheet is completely determined by what happens in the physical one; in particular, as shown in Fig. 2-1, there is also a cut in the unphysical sheet for real $k^2 < -\mu^2/4$. Consequently, we shall confine ourselves to the physical sheet, unless explicitly stated. In particular we shall forbid ourselves to cross the positive k^2 axis without special care.

2-7 PHYSICAL ASPECTS OF THE PARTIAL-WAVE FORMALISM

Let us now see how the analytical knowledge of the partial-wave amplitude which we have gained may be used to get physical predictions. We already have seen an important connection between the location of the left-hand cut and the range of the potential, so that we may grossly expect the low-energy phase shift to vary more rapidly the shorter the interaction range. Connections of this kind will prove more and more important and will be clarified subsequently (cf. Chapters 3 and 5).

Another important connection can be made at this point if we come back to the poles of the amplitude which were indicated in Sec. 2-6. The partial-wave amplitude may be written

$$a_\ell(k^2) = \frac{1}{2ki}\left(e^{2i\delta_\ell} - 1\right) = \frac{1}{2ki}\,\frac{\varphi^-(\ell,k^2) - \varphi^+(\ell,k^2)}{\varphi^+(\ell,k^2)} \qquad (2\text{-}20)$$

This equation indeed gives us analyticity for $a_\ell(k^2)$ wherever $\varphi^\pm(\ell,k^2)$ is analytic, except if $\varphi^+(\ell,k^2)$ vanishes, which may happen for some values of k^2.

Let us see where the corresponding poles are located. Around a value of k^2 corresponding to a pole, the asymptotic form of $u_\ell(k^2,r)$ as expressed by (2-15) is

$$u_\ell(k^2,r) \underset{r\to\infty}{\sim} \varphi^-(\ell,k^2)\, e^{ikr} \qquad (2\text{-}21)$$

If this happens on the physical sheet (i.e., Im $k > 0$), it will be a damped exponential, and therefore a normalizable wave function which must correspond to a physical state. It cannot thus be anything but a bound state. But then the corresponding value of k^2 must be real and negative. Therefore there are poles in the physical sheets which must correspond to the bound states. There are no other poles in that sheet.

On the unphysical sheet, however, there may be poles anywhere, as the form (2-21) defines an explosive exponential (Im $k < 0$), and there is no physical argument to fix its location. (This difference justifies the names of physical and unphysical given to the two sheets.)

Is it possible, anyway, to give a physical interpretation to such a pole? Actually that can be done in a sensible way only if it lies very close to the physical region, i.e., a point like B in Fig. 2-1 with a rather small and negative imaginary part. Such a pole will affect strongly the behavior of the partial-wave amplitude $a_\ell(k^2)$ in the very near physical points which correspond to positive real values of k^2. To see how $a_\ell(k^2)$ behaves in the physical region near the pole, it is useful to use the function $S(\ell,k^2) = e^{2i\delta_\ell} = 1 + 2ika_\ell(k^2)$.

If S has a pole on the unphysical sheet, at $k^2 = k_r^2 - i\Gamma/2$ it means, by (2-18), that it has a zero on the first sheet at the same place. By symmetry, as all the data of the problem are real, it also has a zero on the physical sheet at the complex conjugate point $k^2 = k_r^2 + i\Gamma/2$.

In more detail, the coefficients of the Schrödinger equation being real, the wave function $u_\ell(k^{2*},r)$ is the complex conjugate $[u_\ell(k^2,r)]^*$ of $u_\ell(k^2,r)$. From (2-15) we get $u_\ell(k^{2*},r) \approx \varphi^-(\ell,k^{2*})\, e^{-ik^*r} + \varphi^+(\ell,k^{2*})\, e^{ik^*r}$. [We have changed the signs in the exponentials to take into account the convention about Im k stated immediately after (2-15), which means in fact that $\sqrt{k^{2*}} = -k^*$.] Taking the complex conjugate of both sides, we get

$$u_\ell(k^2,r) \approx [\varphi^-(\ell,k^{2*})]^*\, e^{ikr} + [\varphi^+(\ell,k^{2*})]^*\, e^{-ikr}$$

We have, therefore, $\varphi^\pm(\ell,k^{2*}) = [\varphi^\pm(\ell,k^2)]^*$, which implies $S(\ell,k^{2*}) = [S(\ell,k^2)]^*$. In other words, if $S(k_r^2 - i\Gamma/2) = 0$, then $S(k_r^2 + i\Gamma/2) = 0$. We can then write explicitly the main variation of $S(\ell,k^2)$ in the neighborhood of k_r^2 in the form

$$S(\ell,k^2) = \frac{k^2 - k_r^2 - \dfrac{i\Gamma}{2}}{k^2 - k_r^2 + \dfrac{i\Gamma}{2}}\, S_P(\ell,k^2) \tag{2-22}$$

where Sp is a slowly varying function.

This gives for the phase shift δ_ℓ the expression

$$\delta_\ell = \tan^{-1}\left[\frac{\Gamma}{2(k_r^2 - k^2)}\right] + \delta_{\ell P} \tag{2-23}$$

where $\delta_{\ell P}$ varies slowly. This formula is nothing but the Breit-Wigner expression for the phase shift in the neighborhood of a resonance of energy k_r^2 and width Γ; $\delta_{\ell P}$ is the customary potential phase shift, the first term being the resonant phase shift.

Consequently, a pole at $k^2 = k_r^2 - i\Gamma/2$ in the unphysical sheet, if Γ is not too large, will produce a resonance in scattering with energy k_r^2 and a width Γ.

We may then summarize our findings in the following way: The dynamical singularities of the partial-wave amplitudes (potential-dependent singularities) are:

1. A left-hand cut whose position is associated with the range of the forces.

2. Poles in the physical sheet at the energy of the bound states.

3. Poles anywhere in the unphysical sheets, which may be interpreted as resonances if they are close to the positive real k^2 axis. For completeness, we may mention also the case of the poles on the negative real axis in the unphysical sheet, which correspond to "virtual states" (cf. the singlet neutron-proton scattering at low energy, where there is a pole on the unphysical sheet at a negative energy of ~ 100 keV).

The fact that both bound states and resonances are connected with poles of the partial-wave amplitudes indicates a strong parallelism between these two notions. As is well known, that may be used to interpret a resonance as a metastable bound state as is done, for instance, in the compound nucleus model of N. Bohr.

3

ANALYTIC PROPERTIES IN ENERGY AND MOMENTUM TRANSFORM

Our preceding analysis of the analytic properties of the partial-wave amplitude has lead us to rather simple results and to an interesting correspondance between analytical notions like poles and physical notions like bound states or resonances. It seems then worthwhile to see what we have thus gained in understanding the properties of the full scattering amplitude $f(k^2, \cos\theta)$. Clearly, we shall be lead to introduce complex values of k^2. Moreover, it will be found convenient to introduce also complex values of $\cos\theta$. However, $\cos\theta$ is not the most useful variable and we shall rather use the squared momentum transfer Δ^2, which leads us first to study more precisely the kinematics of scattering.

3-1 KINEMATICS

Let $\mathbf{k}$ be the momentum of the incident particle and $\mathbf{k}'$ that of the outgoing one. We define Δ^2 as $\Delta^2 = (\mathbf{k} - \mathbf{k}')^2$, or

$$\Delta^2 = \mathbf{k}^2 + \mathbf{k}'^2 - 2\mathbf{k}\cdot\mathbf{k}' = 2k^2(1 - \cos\theta) \tag{3-1}$$

The inverse relation reads

$$\cos\theta = 1 - \frac{\Delta^2}{2k^2} \tag{3-2}$$

It will be found convenient to visualize the scattering amplitude $f(k^2, \cos\theta)$ as a function of $f(k^2, \Delta^2)$ and, when the two variables k^2 and Δ^2 are real, to use a representation of the (k^2, Δ^2) plane.

On such a plot the physical values of k^2 are the positive real ones, and as the values of $\cos\theta$ are between -1 and $+1$ one has $0 \le \Delta^2 \le 4k^2$.

It is convenient to picture this region as in Fig. 3-1, where the shaded region is the physical domain of variation of k^2 and Δ^2 (note that the Δ^2 axis is oriented downward). We note from (3-1) that a constant value of $\cos\theta$ is represented by a straight line going through the origin (see in particular the limits of the physical region $\cos\theta = \pm 1$). The fact that the width of the physical region decreases as the energy goes down reflects the diminishing of the phase space. We introduce a new notation for the scattering amplitude, to express it directly in terms of k^2 and Δ^2:

$$f(k^2, \cos\theta) = f\left(k^2,\ 1 - \frac{\Delta^2}{2k^2}\right) = F(k^2,\Delta^2)$$

It will be now our problem to investigate the analytic properties of this function F.

3-2 ANALYTIC PROPERTIES IN ENERGY

We may expect that $F(k^2,\Delta^2)$ has analyticity properties as a function of k^2, as each partial-wave amplitude has some. It is not trivial, however, to see what the whole domain of analyticity is, *for fixed* Δ^2, as the convergence of the series (2-11) would have to be studied carefully.

$$\begin{aligned} F(k^2,\Delta^2) &= \Sigma(2\ell + 1)a_\ell(k^2)P_\ell(\cos\theta) \\ &= \Sigma(2\ell + 1)a_\ell(k^2)P_\ell\left(1 - \frac{\Delta^2}{2k^2}\right) \qquad (2\text{-}11) \end{aligned}$$

Instead of following this method, which would in fact fail, we shall give

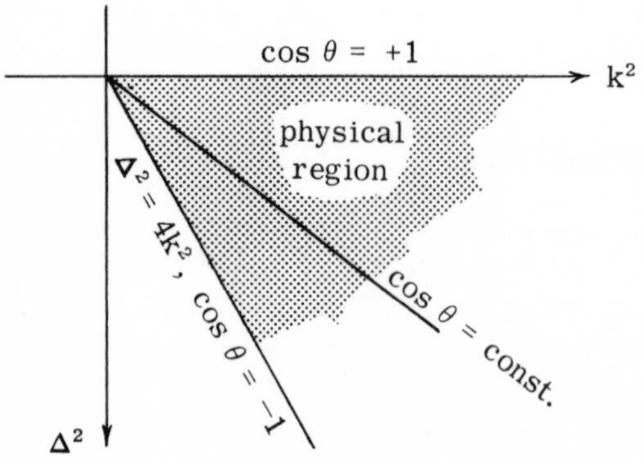

Figure 3-1

an idea of the result by a completely different approach. We do not attempt to give any proof of the results stated, but simply to give plausibility arguments. It is comforting, however, to know that the results stated in this chapter can be proved, by still other methods, which demand a higher mathematical apparatus.

The approach we follow in this chapter is to consider the Born series for the scattering amplitude, as given by (1-29), and to analyze the analytic properties of each separate term. We then assume that the analytic properties of the scattering amplitude are the properties of the sum of the Born series

$$-4\pi f(\mathbf{k}'\cdot\mathbf{k}) = \langle k' | V | k \rangle + \frac{1}{(2\pi)^3} \int \langle k' | V | p \rangle \frac{d^3p}{(k+i\varepsilon)^2 - \mathbf{p}^2} \times \langle p | V | k \rangle + \frac{1}{(2\pi)^6} \int \langle k' | V | p_1 \rangle \frac{d^3p_1}{(k+i\varepsilon)^2 - p_1^2} \times \langle p_1 | V | p_2 \rangle \frac{d^3p_1}{(k+i\varepsilon)^2 - p_2^2} \langle p_2 | V | k \rangle + \cdots \qquad (1\text{-}29)$$

without worrying about whether or not that series actually converges.

We shall first consider the simple case where the potential is a pure Yukawa potential

$$V(r) = g\,\frac{e^{-\mu r}}{r}$$

In order to write explicitly the Born series (1-29) it is first necessary to evaluate the matrix elements $\langle p | V | p' \rangle$, i.e.,

$$\langle p | V | p' \rangle = g \int e^{i(\mathbf{p}-\mathbf{p}')\mathbf{x}}\, \frac{e^{-\mu r}}{r}\, d^3x$$

This integral is easy to compute in spherical coordinates, where it reads

$$\langle p | V | p' \rangle = g \int e^{i|\mathbf{p}-\mathbf{p}'| r \cos\theta - \mu r}\, r^2\, dr\, d(\cos\theta)\, d\varphi$$

The integration over φ is trivial, and that over $\cos\theta$ simple, so that one gets

$$\langle p | V | p' \rangle = 2\pi g \int_0^\infty \left\{ \frac{e^{i|\mathbf{p}-\mathbf{p}'|r} - e^{-i|\mathbf{p}-\mathbf{p}'|r}}{i|\mathbf{p}-\mathbf{p}'|r} \right\} e^{-\mu r}\, r\, dr$$

The last integration is also very simple, so that finally

$$\langle p|V|p'\rangle = \frac{2\pi g}{i|p-p'|}\left\{\frac{1}{\mu - i|p-p'|} - \frac{1}{\mu + i|p-p'|}\right\}$$

$$= \frac{4\pi g}{(p-p')^2 + \mu^2}$$

That result can now readily be inserted into the Born series and gives

$$F(k^2,\Delta^2) = -\sum_{n=1}^{\infty} F_n(k^2,\Delta^2) \tag{3-3}$$

with

$$F_1(k^2,\Delta^2) = \frac{4\pi g}{\Delta^2 + \mu^2} \tag{3-4a}$$

$$F_2(k^2,\Delta^2) = \frac{2g^2}{\pi}\int \frac{d\mathbf{p}}{[(\mathbf{k}' - \mathbf{p})^2 + \mu^2][\mathbf{k}^2 - \mathbf{p}^2 + i\varepsilon][(\mathbf{p} - \mathbf{k})^2 + \mu^2]} \tag{3-4b}$$

$$F_3(k^2,\Delta^2) = \frac{g^3}{\pi^3}\iint \frac{d\mathbf{p}_1\, d\mathbf{p}_2}{[(\mathbf{k}' - \mathbf{p}_1)^2 + \mu^2][\mathbf{k}^2 - \mathbf{p}_1^2 + i\varepsilon][(\mathbf{p}_1 - \mathbf{p}_2)^2 + \mu^2][\mathbf{k}^2 - \mathbf{p}_2^2 + i\varepsilon][(\mathbf{p}_2 - \mathbf{k})^2 + \mu^2]} \tag{3-4c}$$

and so on.

The first term is very simple; in fact, it is independent of k^2 and therefore, for fixed Δ^2, it is analytic in k^2.

Analytic properties of the other terms are less easy to see. The corresponding integrals will be well defined and analytic in k^2 and Δ^2 as long as the denominators do not vanish. This condition shows immediately that there is a singularity on the positive k^2 axis, since there are denominators like $k^2 - p^2$ which will vanish for some value of p^2 since p^2 varies from zero to infinity. This is the right-hand cut which we have found previously for the partial-wave amplitudes.

It is also apparent that, as long as the imaginary parts of $\mathbf{k}$ and $\mathbf{k}'$ are kept small enough, the denominators of the type $(\mathbf{k} - \mathbf{p})^2 + \mu^2$ coming from the potential cannot vanish, since that would require (with $\mathbf{k} = \mathbf{k}_1 + i\mathbf{k}_2$)

$$(\mathbf{p} - \mathbf{k}_1)^2 - \mathbf{k}_2^2 + \mu^2 = 0$$

$$\mathbf{p}\cdot\mathbf{k}_1 = 0$$

and the first equality requires that at least $\mathbf{k}_2^2$ be bigger than μ^2.

Unfortunately this limitation on k_2^2 is not very restrictive. To find analytic properties in a larger region would involve more complicated mathematical methods which we do not want to develop here (e.g., to change the real integration path over the $\mathbf{p}_i$ into a complex one, or to carry out part of the integrations by Feynman's method).

Let us simply state the simple results that can be proved in this way: for fixed nonnegative values of Δ^2, each term of the series (3-3) is analytic in k^2 everywhere except on the right-hand cut.

3-3 ANALYTIC PROPERTIES IN MOMENTUM TRANSFER

The analytic properties of $F(k^2,\Delta^2)$ as a function of Δ^2 are more complicated, and they are not easy to deduce from expression (3-4). It is important, however, to study their physical meaning, as we shall see that the singularities in Δ^2 may lie fairly close to the physical region.

The first singularity, and the simplest, is displayed by the first term of the Born series $F_1(k^2,\Delta^2)$, as given in (3-4a). It is a pole at $\Delta^2 = -\mu^2$. This is clearly a potential-dependent, or dynamical, singularity. The fact that this singularity be a simple pole is uniquely related to the fact that we considered explicitly a single Yukawa potential (an exponential potential would, for example, yield a double pole). The position of that pole is determined by the range of the potential: the longer the range, the smaller μ is, and the closer the pole is to the physical region. (A limiting case is the Coulomb potential, where the potential is α/r of the Yukawa type with $\mu = 0$. In that case the singularity is just in the forward direction, at $\Delta^2 = 0$, i.e., at the edge of the physical region.)

To understand the singularities of the other terms of the Born series (3-3), it is best to recall the physical meaning we gave to them: the term F_n corresponds to n successive scatterings by the potential. Our treatment will actually completely lack rigor, and we give it just to show how complex singularities may be understood in a physical sense. One can view the fact that the first term F_1 is infinite for $\Delta^2 = -\mu^2$ as meaning that many particles go away with an *unphysical* momentum transfer $\Delta^2 = -\mu^2$ since the scattering amplitude appears to be infinite in that case. It is to be expected that if they scatter again, they will again give rise to the same momentum transfer $i\mu$.

This second transfer does not take place in general in the same space direction, and the pole singularity will be washed out, except at the boundary of the possible region, where the two momenta add exactly and correspond to a momentum transfer of $2i\mu$. Therefore, we expect F_2 to have a singularity at $\Delta^2 = -4\mu^2$. In the same way F_n will have a singularity at $\Delta^2 = -n^2\mu^2$.

But life is not so simple, and there is another way to generate singularities: consider the angle instead of the momentum. A singularity at $\Delta^2 = -\mu^2$ is also a singularity at an (unphysical) angle θ_0 determined by $\cos\theta_0 = 1 - (\Delta^2/2k^2) = 1 + (\mu^2/2k^2)$ [cf. (3-2)].

Let us reason as if this angle were physical. The particles scattered once make a kind of a halo, a cone of half-angle θ_0, around the forward direction, where the scattering is very intense. If they scatter again, the particles which would have come out in the halo scatter again preferentially by an angle θ_0, and are smoothly distributed inside a cone of half-angle $2\theta_0$ (see Fig. 3-2). At the surface of this cone, however, there is an enhancement of the scattered particles again, which corresponds to a singularity, at a scattering angle of $2\theta_0$. The mechanism is very similar to the previous one, but the resulting singularity is at a different place. In fact using (3-1) and (3-2) we have

$$\cos\theta_0 = 1 + \frac{\mu^2}{2k^2} \qquad \cos 2\theta_0 = 2\cos^2\theta_0 - 1 = 1 + \frac{2\mu^2}{k^2} + \frac{\mu^4}{2k^4}$$

$$\Delta^2 = 2k^2(1 - \cos 2\theta_0) = -4\mu^2 - \frac{\mu^4}{k^2}$$

This last singularity, and the singularity at $\Delta^2 = -4\mu^2$, are the only ones for F_2. F_3 has three: one at $\Delta^2 = -9\mu^2$, one at $\cos 3\theta_0$, and one coming from a mixture of the two mechanisms: a combination of the singularity at $\Delta^2 = -4\mu^2$ after the first two scatterings and of the singularity due to the third scattering, combined with the law of addition of angles, not of momenta. F_4 has five singular points, and the number of singularities of F_n increases more rapidly than any power of n. It is possible to write down the exact location of each, and they all correspond to negative real values of Δ^2, $\Delta^2 < -4\mu^2$.

We thus get an infinite number of singularities on curves, the

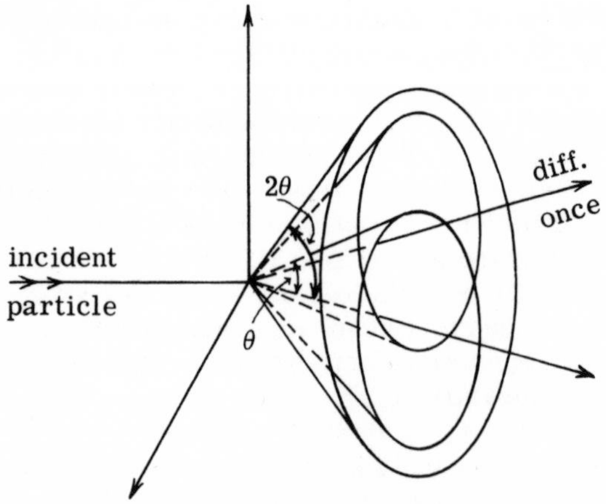

Figure 3-2

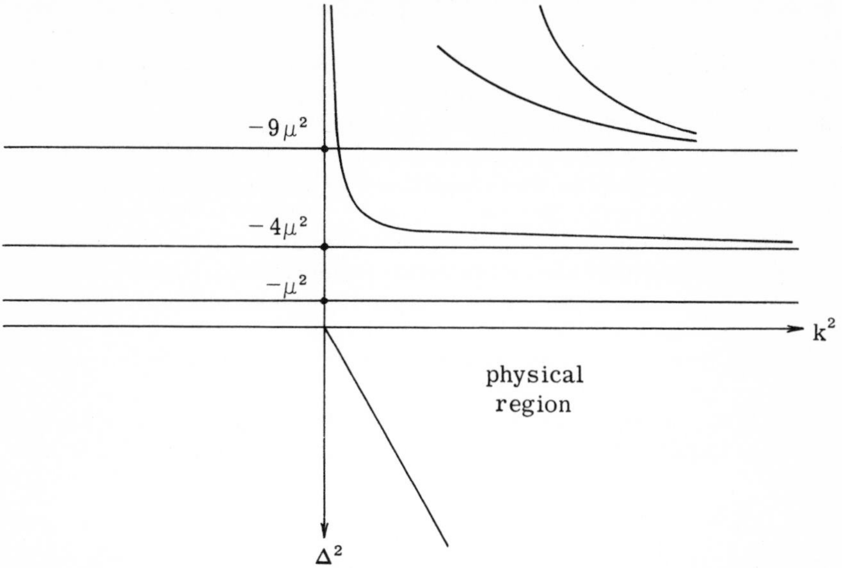

Figure 3-3

so-called Landau curves, which are depicted in Fig. 3-3, to be compared with Fig. 3-2. It happens that all singularities belonging to F_n cluster asymptotically for large k^2 at $\Delta^2 = -n^2\mu^2$.

For values of k^2 other than those on the positive real axis, the only singularities are those independent of k^2, that is, $\Delta^2 = -n^2\mu^2$. The net result is that we have analyticity of $F(k^2,\Delta^2)$ as a function of Δ^2 for all values of k^2 and Δ^2 except for real $\Delta^2 \leq -4\mu^2$, and for a pole at $\Delta^2 = -\mu^2$, as pictured in Fig. 3-3. If we had considered a superposition of several Yukawa potentials, we would of course have several poles, each at the relevant value of Δ^2, and the detailed structure of the other singularities would obviously be much more complicated, but nothing essential would be changed. Had we considered instead a continuous superposition in the form $V(r) = \int_{\mu_0}^{\mu_1} e^{-\mu r}/r\rho(\mu)\, d\mu$, then we would not have poles anymore but a continuous line of singularities along the negative Δ^2 axis (i.e., the previous pole at $\Delta^2 = -\mu^2$ will be spread out between $-\mu_0^2$ and $-\mu_1^2$, giving rise to a cut).

We observe that we may avoid all the singularities in the Δ^2 variable by simply keeping away from the negative Δ^2 axis, i.e., we may imagine that the Δ^2 plane is cut there, and that we have no right to cross this cut, at least when there are other singularities than poles.

3-4 TREATMENT OF EXCHANGE FORCES

We know that in many practical problems, as in nucleon-nucleon scattering, there are not only direct forces but also exchange forces. How will our result be affected by this modification?

We recall what we mean by exchange: The exchange potential operator V_{ex} acts on the wave function $\Psi(x)$ according to: $V_{ex}\Psi(x) = V^e(x)\Psi(-x)$.

It is possible to reduce this case to the preceding one by using a trick: consider first even wave functions only: $\Psi(x) = \Psi(-x)$; when acting on these functions, V_{ex} is equivalent to an ordinary potential:

$$V_{ex}\Psi(x) = V^e(x)\Psi(-x) = V^e(x)\Psi(x)$$

Thus, if the incoming wave contains only even angular momenta, it is possible to solve the scattering problem as for an effective potential

$$V^+(x) = V(x) + V^e(x)$$

and one gets the right answer for the part of the scattering amplitude which is even with respect to the interchange of particles.

If we call $f^+(k^2, \cos\theta)$ the complete scattering amplitude which is obtained from the potential $V^+(x)$ by solving the complete Schrödinger equation, we have therefore equality between the even parts of $f(k^2, \cos\theta)$ and $f^+(k^2, \cos\theta)$, i.e.,

$$\tfrac{1}{2}[f(k^2, \cos\theta) + f(k^2, -\cos\theta)] = \tfrac{1}{2}[f^+(k^2, \cos\theta) + f^+(k^2, -\cos\theta)] \qquad (3\text{-}5)$$

In the same way, when the incoming wave is odd, then

$$V_{ex}\Psi(x) = V^e(x)\Psi(-x) = -V^e(x)\Psi(x)$$

so that the scattering is defined by an effective potential:

$$V^-(x) = V(x) - V^e(x)$$

to which corresponds a Schrödinger equation $[\Delta + k^2 - V^-(x)]\Psi^-(x) = 0$ which leads to a scattering amplitude $f^-(k^2, \cos\theta)$. The odd parts of that amplitude and of $f(k^2, \cos\theta)$ coincide, so that

$$\tfrac{1}{2}[f(k^2, \cos\theta) - f(k^2, -\cos\theta)] = \tfrac{1}{2}[f^-(k^2, \cos\theta) - f^-(k^2, -\cos\theta)] \qquad (3\text{-}6)$$

Adding (3-5) and (3-6) we get

$$f(k^2, \cos\theta) = \tfrac{1}{2}[f^+(k^2, \cos\theta) + f^+(k^2, -\cos\theta) + f^-(k^2, \cos\theta) - f^-(k^2, -\cos\theta)] \qquad (3\text{-}7)$$

If we notice that changing $\cos\theta$ into $-\cos\theta$ is the same as changing Δ^2 into $4k^2 - \Delta^2$, we may write (3-7) as

$$F(k^2,\Delta^2) = \tfrac{1}{2}[F^+(k^2,\Delta^2) + F^+(k^2, 4k^2 - \Delta^2) + F^-(k^2,\Delta^2) - F^-(k^2, 4k^2 - \Delta^2)] \qquad (3\text{-}8)$$

Clearly, the amplitudes $F^+(k^2,\Delta^2)$ and $F^-(k^2,\Delta^2)$ have the analytic properties that we established in the preceding section; i.e., they are analytic except for singularities occurring for real positive k^2 or for real negative Δ^2. It is easy to deduce from this result that $F^+(k^2, 4k^2 - \Delta^2)$ and $F^-(k^2, 4k^2 - \Delta^2)$ will have the same k^2 singularity and other singularities for negative values of $k^2 - \Delta^2$. For instance, a pole $1/(\Delta^2 + \mu^2)$ in $F^+(k^2,\Delta^2)$ will lead to a pole $1/(4k^2 - \Delta^2 + \mu^2)$ in $F^+(k^2, 4k^2 - \Delta^2)$, which will be represented in Fig. 3-4 by a straight line parallel to the backward boundary of the physical region. In fact, this is quite natural, since the pole $\Delta^2 = -\mu^2$ was on a straight line parallel to the forward boundary of the physical region and since exchange replaces $\cos\theta$ by $-\cos\theta$. More generally, we shall immediately get the picture of singularities in Fig. 3-4 by this replacement. It is to be noted that the amplitudes $f^+(k^2, \cos\theta)$ and $f^-(k^2, \cos\theta)$, when expanded into partial waves by (2-13), give the right answers $a_\ell^+(k^2)$ for even ℓ and $a_\ell^-(k^2)$ for odd ℓ.

3-5 BOUND STATES

If the potential is large enough and attractive, we expect that bound states will appear. We have seen in Sec. 2-7 that in such a case there appears a pole in the partial-wave amplitude $a_\ell(k^2)$ which has the same angular momentum ℓ as the bound state, at the negative value of k^2 which is the energy $k^2 = -B$ of the bound state (B being the binding energy). This pole will appear in the total amplitude as shown by the partial-wave expansion (HI) of $f(k^2, \cos\theta)$. In fact, in the neighborhood of $k^2 = -B$, $a_\ell(k^2)$ will be essentially of the form $N/(k^2 + B)$, so that the total amplitude will appear as

$$f(k^2, \cos\theta) = (2\ell + 1)\frac{N}{k^2 + B}P_\ell(\cos\theta) + \text{regular function}$$

or (3-9)

$$F(k^2,\Delta^2) = (2\ell + 1)\frac{N}{k^2 + B}P_\ell\left(1 - \frac{\Delta^2}{2k^2}\right) + \text{regular function}$$

It is impossible to find such a behavior for any of the terms of the Born series (3-3). This shows why this series has to diverge at least as soon as there are bound states, and also the care which must be applied if one is to reason from the analytic properties of the Born terms to get the analytic properties of the total amplitude. All the results we have stated up to now have been actually proved by other methods, however, starting from the Schrödinger equation. We developed the Born expansion analysis just because it is the only tool we have to date for the study of the relativistic S-matrix theory. Here the general neat result is that, in the case of potential scattering, there exist all the singularities we have mentioned, and no more.

We may, to conclude this chapter, draw a chart of all the singularities (Fig. 3-5). The solid lines are singularities, the dashed ones

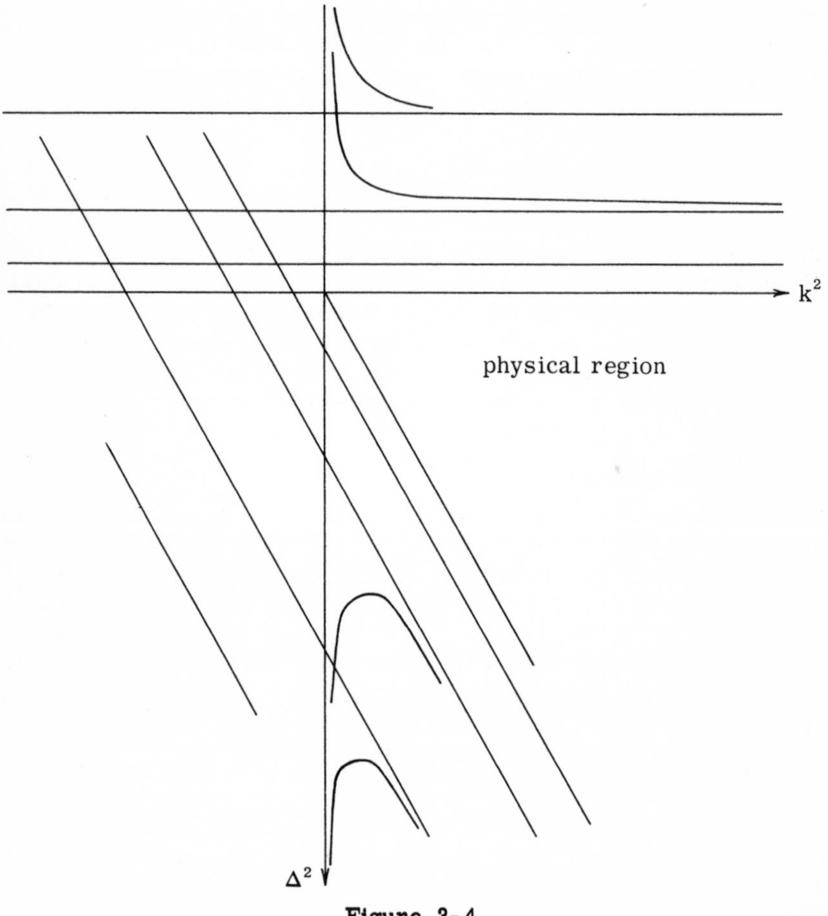

Figure 3-4

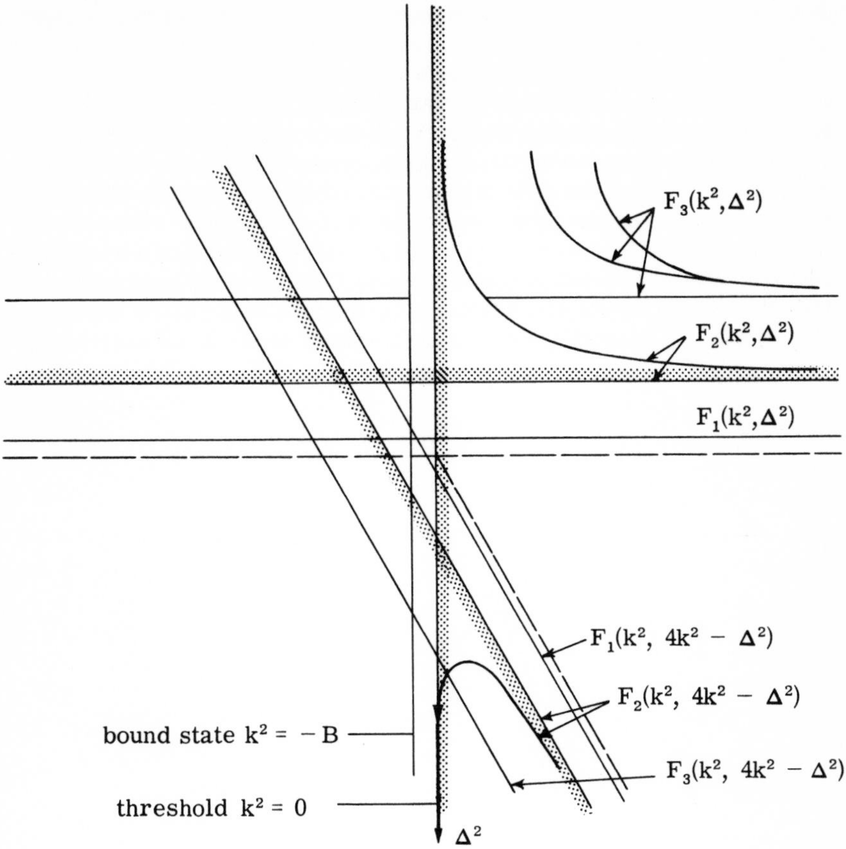

Figure 3-5

indicate the kinematics (Fig. 3-1). The shading along the singularities at $k^2 = 0$, $\Delta^2 = -4\mu^2$, and $\Delta^2 = -4k^2 - 4\mu^2$ indicates that in fact these singularities are the start of cuts extending to infinity. We have three cuts, which go through all the singularities. This is possible because the singularities are all located on the following surfaces:

k^2 real and positive, Δ^2 arbitrary

Δ^2 real and $\Delta^2 < -4\mu^2$, k^2 arbitrary

$4k^2 - \Delta^2$ real and $4k^2 - \Delta^2 < -4\mu^2$, k^2 arbitrary

If we forbid ourselves to cross these surfaces, thus making cuts in the Δ^2,k^2 complex space, we avoid crossing any singularity. The cause of each singularity is indicated. We have indicated one bound state pole, but there may be several.

The results we have found allow us to treat the amplitude $F(k^2, \Delta^2)$ as an analytic function of its two arguments. They are not very useful in the case of potential scattering, since it is always possible to get all physically relevant information directly from the Schrödinger equation. The interest in these analytic properties lies in fact in the possibility of extending them to the case of relativistic interactions. In that case, we do not know to write a Schrödinger equation and the analytic properties which clearly relate "dynamical" singularities with the properties of the scattering amplitude could allow us to obtain dynamical properties of the elementary particle interactions.

4

INTRODUCTION OF COMPLEX ANGULAR MOMENTA

This chapter will seem to be of purely academic interest to the reader who has never heard of "Regge poles" and of the interest they generate these years in strong-interactions physics. The methods developed here have been useful in a very different field of physics: the propagation of radio waves around the earth. It is a strange fate that they should turn out to be useful in relativistic strong-interactions physics. We therefore ask the reader to suspend his "why?" until the end of Chapter 6, where, we hope, he will see the need for this kind of method.

4-1 INTERPOLATION BETWEEN PHYSICAL VALUES OF ANGULAR MOMENTUM

Consider two very different kinds of potentials: the Coulomb potential and the three-dimensional harmonic oscillator potential. They have several features in common: they are exactly solvable, and they have an infinite number of bound states, most of which are degenerate. It is customary to label the bound states by the angular momentum ℓ, the magnetic quantum number m, and a "total" quantum number n, which is simply the rank of the state in the energy sequence. It is clear that this total quantum number is something rather odd: a small perturbation splits the degeneracy of the levels and therefore one would have to modify completely the definition of the total quantum number. On the other hand, there is, in the case of the harmonic oscillator, a strange relation, that is, $\ell - n$ has to be even. So n has not much of a physical meaning.

Sometimes n is replaced by the "internal" quantum number, which is the number of nodes of the radial wave function, and therefore has a chance to be more significant. Let us plot the values of the energy and angular momentum of the bound states on a (ℓ, k^2) plot as shown in Fig. 4-1. We draw smooth lines joining states with the same internal quantum number, for three cases (Fig. 4-1): Coulomb, harmonic oscillator, and infinite spherical square-well potentials. We note that, in the last case, we would not know how to define a total quantum number, but that the lines corresponding to constant internal quantum number are very smooth. Is it then possible to interpolate in some sense these lines in a well-defined fashion?

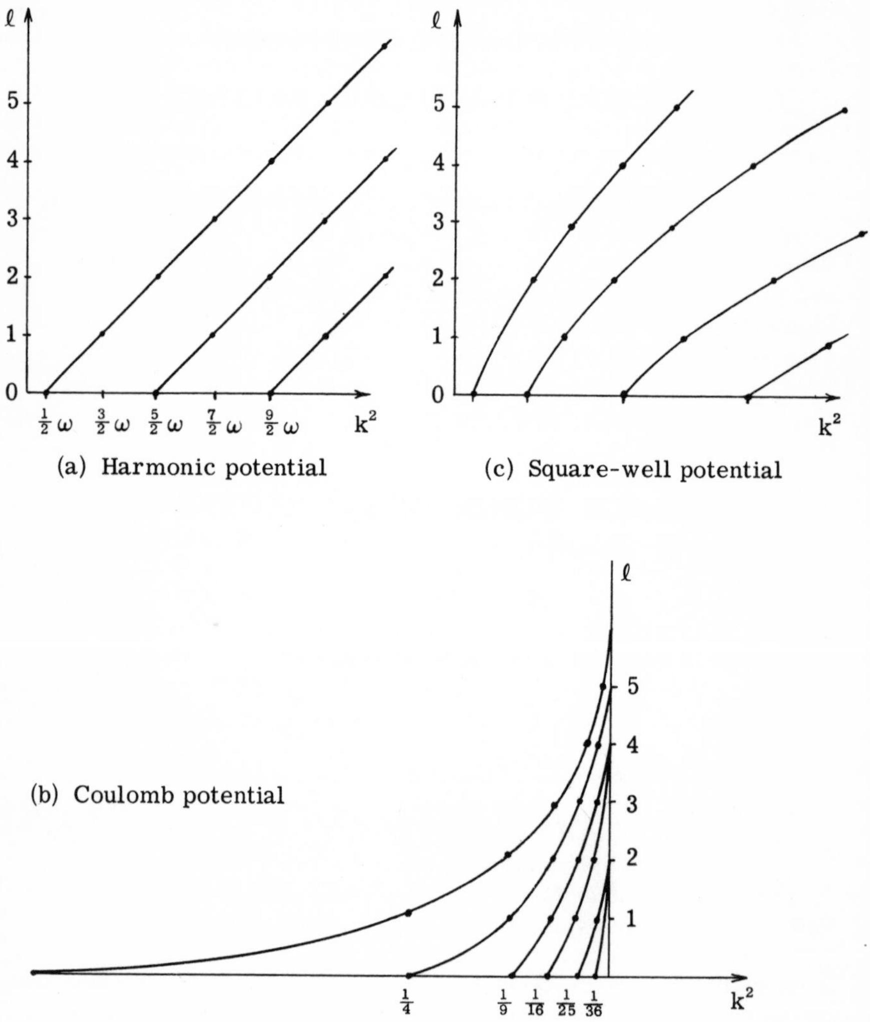

Figure 4-1

The easiest way to make this interpolation appears to be to vary ℓ in the radial Schrödinger equation. If one considers ℓ as a parameter, the radial equation has still solutions, which may still be labeled by the number of nodes, as long as ℓ stays real. This allows one to give a precise definition to the interpolation curves shown in Fig. 4-1.

We are not interested, however, in such pathological potentials as the infinite wells, either harmonic or square. In strong-interactions physics we are not even interested in potentials with an infinite number of bound states. Let us analyze for its own sake how this interpolation would be made with the Yukawa potential we have considered until now.

Practically the whole of Chapter 2 goes through in the same way, whether or not ℓ is an integer. In particular, the Jost functions $\varphi^{\pm}(\ell,k^2)$ are analytic functions of ℓ as they were of k^2, for the same reason: the solutions of a differential equation are practically always analytic functions of the parameters (Poincaré's theorem). The bound states are given by the zeroes of $\varphi^{+}(\ell,k^2)$ (Sec. 2-7), and therefore we still get curves of interpolation by solving the equation $\varphi^{+}(\ell,k^2) = 0$ with respect to ℓ. Let us denote a solution by $\ell = \alpha(k^2)$.

For negative real k^2, $\varphi^{+}(\ell,k^2)$ is real for ℓ real,† and the function $\ell = \alpha(k^2)$ is real. For positive real k^2, $\varphi^{+}(\ell,k^2)$ is not real any more, and the solution $\ell = \alpha(k^2)$ becomes in general complex.

We have thus to consider not only noninteger values of ℓ but also complex ones. This extension allows $a_\ell(k^2)$ as defined by (2-20) to be considered as a function of both complex ℓ and k^2, which is analytic in ℓ except at the zeroes $\ell = \alpha(k^2)$ of $\varphi^{+}(\ell,k^2)$. These zeroes are poles for $a_\ell(k^2)$, and are named after Regge, who first introduced them into the field of strong interactions.

The functions $\ell = \alpha(k^2)$ are in general called Regge pole trajectories. We shall see a number of examples in Sec. 4-4.

4-2 THE SOMMERFELD-WATSON FORMULA

We know already that whenever a Regge pole goes through an integer value of ℓ, it corresponds to a bound state at precisely that energy. In fact, that is how we introduced the whole concept of noninteger angular momentum.

To get a more quantitative connection, we have to introduce a formula currently called the Sommerfeld-Watson formula. It is derived from the expansion (2-11):

---

† For k^2 real and negative, the wave function $u_\ell(k^2,r)$ is real, and, if we define $K = \sqrt{-k^2}$, the exponentials $e^{\pm Kr}$ in the asymptotic form of $u_\ell(k^2,r)$ are real, so that the coefficients of these exponentials, i.e., the Jost functions, have to be real.

$$f(k^2, \cos\theta) = \sum_{\ell=0}^{\infty} (2\ell + 1) a_\ell(k^2) P_\ell(\cos\theta) \tag{4-1}$$

We may observe that all functions of ℓ in the right-hand side may be interpolated by analytic functions of ℓ, $a_\ell(k^2)$ by the "partial-wave amplitude" defined by the radial equation, where ℓ is taken as an arbitrary parameter. $P_\ell(\cos\theta)$ may be defined also as an analytic function of ℓ: it is the solution of the Legendre equation, which is regular and equal to 1 at $\cos\theta = 1$. It is not a polynomial for noninteger ℓ, but a "hypergeometric function" with a branch cut going from -1 to $-\infty$.

There is a very general procedure then, if one has a series of which all terms are analytic functions of the index, which is to view it a sum over residues of poles in the following way: Consider the function

$$\frac{(2\ell + 1) a_\ell(k^2) P_\ell(\cos\theta)}{\sin \Pi\ell}$$

as a function of ℓ. It has poles at each integer coming from the zeroes of $\sin \Pi\ell$. It also has poles for noninteger ℓ, which are the Regge poles of $a_\ell(k^2)$. If we encircle all positive integers by a contour C_1, Fig. 4-2, and integrate with respect to ℓ along C_1, we can deform the contour of integration and split it into small circles around the integer. The integral around each can be calculated by Cauchy's formula. We get, up to a factor of $2i(-1)^{\ell+1}$, the terms of the series (4-1). The factor $-2i$ is harmless, but the factor of $(-1)^\ell$ has to be taken care of.

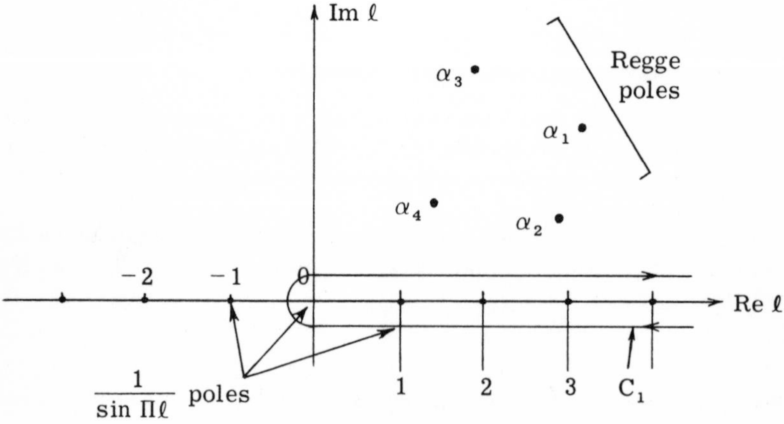

Figure 4-2

This is possible by writing $P_\ell(-\cos\theta) = (-1)^\ell P_\ell(\cos\theta)$ for integer ℓ. We then end up with the formula

$$f(k^2, \cos\theta) = \frac{i}{2}\int_{C_1} \frac{(2\ell+1)\,a_\ell(k^2)P_\ell(-\cos\theta)}{\sin \Pi\ell}\, d\ell \qquad (4\text{-}2)$$

The main interest of this Sommerfeld-Watson representation of the amplitude is that we are still free to change the integration path C_1 by continuous deformation. Usually, it is deformed as shown in Fig. 4-3 into a contour C which has the advantage of putting in evidence the individual contributions of the Regge poles. Indeed, each contribution may be calculated by using Cauchy's formula. As before

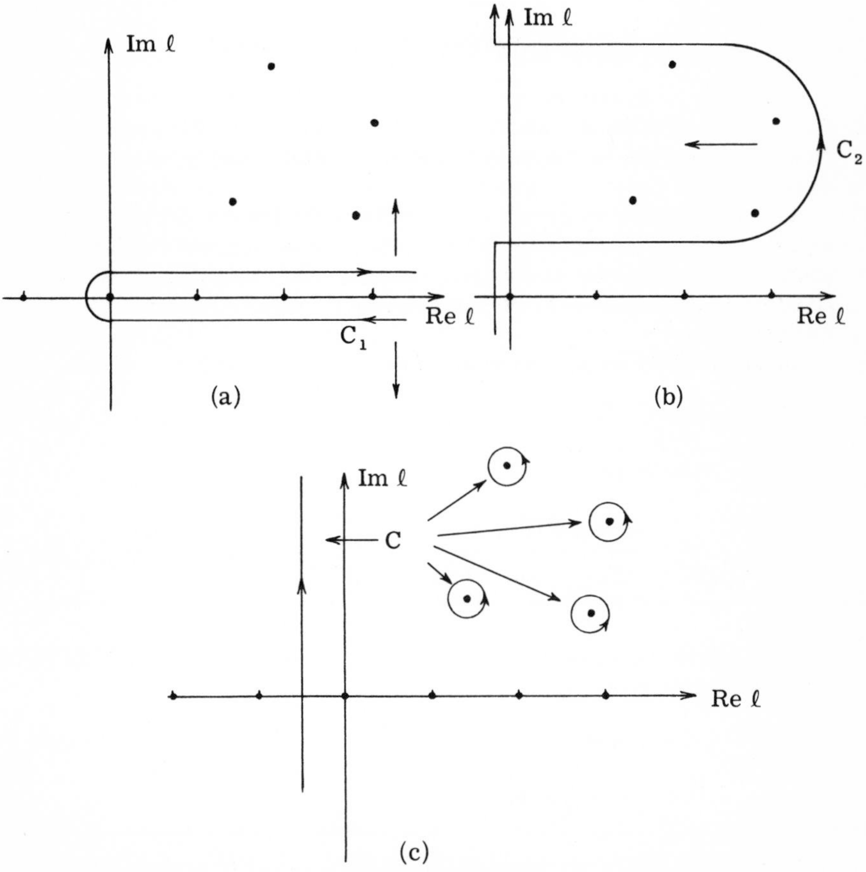

Figure 4-3

we call $\alpha_i(k^2)$ the different solutions $\ell = \alpha_i(k^2)$ of $\varphi^+(\ell, k^2) = 0$, which give the locations of Regge poles, and get

$$f(k^2, \cos\theta) = \frac{i}{2}\int_{-1/2-i\infty}^{-1/2+i\infty} \frac{(2\ell+1)a_\ell(k^2)P_\ell(-\cos\theta)\, d\ell}{\sin \Pi\ell}$$

$$+\sum_i \frac{\beta_i(k^2)P_{\alpha_i(k^2)}(-\cos\theta)}{\sin \Pi\alpha_i(k^2)} \qquad (4\text{-}3)$$

where $\beta_i(k^2)$ stands for the integral $(2\ell + 1)a_\ell(k^2)\, d\ell$ around the pole α_i.

4-3 PHYSICAL INTERPRETATION OF REGGE POLES

Formula (4-3) allows one to analyze explicitly the contribution to the total amplitude of each Regge pole individually. We should then be able to find the properties of the bound states again, starting with this formula.

Let us consider a typical Regge pole contribution, dropping the index i: $\beta(k^2)P_{\alpha(k^2)}(\cos\theta)/\sin \Pi\alpha(k^2)$. The bound-state poles occur whenever α becomes an integer, owing to the vanishing of $\sin \Pi\alpha$. Assume that this occurs for some value k_ℓ^2 of k^2, for which $\alpha(k_\ell^2) = \ell$, integer.

In the vicinity of k_ℓ^2, we may write

$$\frac{\beta(k^2)P_{\alpha(k^2)}(-\cos\theta)}{\sin \Pi\alpha(k^2)}$$

$$= \frac{\beta(k_\ell^2)P_\ell(-\cos\theta)}{\Pi \frac{\partial\alpha}{\partial k^2}(k_\ell^2)\cdot(k^2 - k_\ell^2)\cos \Pi\ell} + \text{regular function} \qquad (4\text{-}4)$$

We find again the same form for the bound-state pole as in (3-9) with the identification

$$N = \frac{\beta(k_\ell^2)}{(2\ell+1)\Pi \frac{\partial\alpha}{\partial k^2}(k_\ell^2)}$$

Another case where we suspect that a physical interpretation can be given is when a Regge pole, instead of going straight through an integer

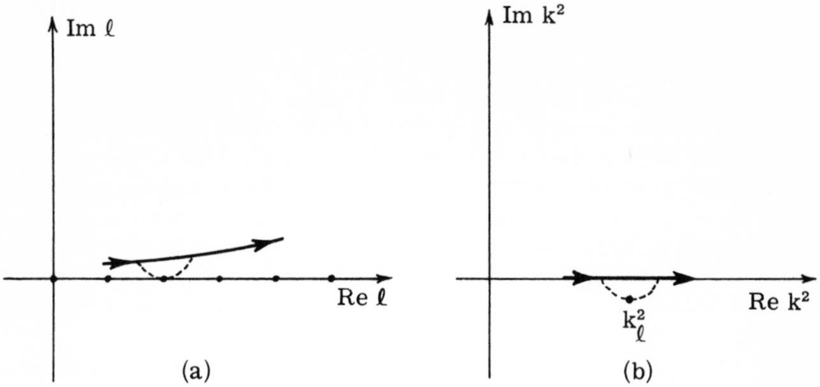

Figure 4-4

(physical) value of ℓ, goes nearby as k^2 varies on the positive real (physical) axis.

We have drawn in Fig. 4-4a an assumed trajectory (solid line), and in Fig. 4-4b the corresponding values of k^2 (solid line along the real axis). As the function $\ell = \alpha(k^2)$ is analytic, a classical theorem of function theory tells us that the correspondence between the ℓ plane and the k^2 plane is a "conformal mapping"; that is, all the angles are preserved. If we distort the k^2 path into the dashed one, the ℓ path will also be distorted with the same angle (dashed line in Fig. 4-4a), and we easily see that at the complex point k_ℓ^2, $\alpha(k_\ell^2) = \ell$, and (4-4) again applies. But k_ℓ^2 is on the unphysical sheet† (see Fig. 2-1, point B). All this ends up finally in a pole in the ℓ-th partial wave on the unphysical sheet, and this is a resonance (see Sec. 2-7).

We have our choice then of taking a physical ℓ with an unphysical k^2 (resonance, dashed line in Fig. 4-4) or an unphysical ℓ with a physical k^2 (solid line in Fig. 4-4). To this last choice corresponds a description of a metastable state which is different from the conventional one and which is called a "shadow state." In such a description, the radial wave function is very acceptable. As $\varphi^+(\ell,k^2) = 0$, the asymptotic form of $u_\ell(k^2,r)$ shows that the wave function is purely outgoing, as it should be for a decaying state. The angular wave function, however, is not very pleasant, as all the Legendre functions have singular points on the sphere for noninteger ℓ. However, there are locally perfectly smooth solutions, and these have a decaying character, owing to the fact that the centrifugal term $\ell(\ell + 1)/r^2$ has an

---

†*Note:* The structure of the right-hand cut is slightly more complicated when ℓ is permitted to take on complex values than in Chapter 2, but this does not change the present reasoning.

imaginary, absorptive, part in the angular equation, corresponding to its counterpart $-\ell(\ell + 1)/r^2$, which creates the outgoing wave, in the radial equation. This is easier to see on a two-dimensional model, where a complex angular momentum m gives an angular wave function $e^{im\varphi}$, with m complex. Such a wave function represents the decay of the metastable state as it rotates, giving rise to the purely outgoing radial wave function. In the old problem of Sommerfeld, where he studied the propagation around the earth of radio waves, this exponential decay beyond the horizon (tunnel effect) was the main phenomenon studied, and nobody cared about what happened very far from the antenna. The pole with the smallest imaginary part (slowest decay) gave practically the answer.

It is of course more difficult to feel why this kind of approach should be interesting for strong-interactions physics and, indeed, the most interesting pole will turn out to be that with the largest real part, in contradistinction to Sommerfeld's case.

4-4 BEHAVIOR OF REGGE TRAJECTORIES

Let us now give an idea of the behavior of Regge poles. The least pathological of the potentials we considered in Fig. 4-1 is the Coulomb potential. It is the only one among those three which has a scattering amplitude. The Coulomb phase shifts, which are given in many textbooks of quantum mechanics, lead to

$$1 + 2ika_\ell(k^2) = S(\ell, k^2) = \frac{\Gamma(\ell + 1 + i\gamma)}{\Gamma(\ell + 1 - i\gamma)}$$

where Γ is Euler's gamma function and

$$\gamma = \frac{Z_1 Z_2 e^2 m}{\hbar^2 k} = \frac{-\lambda}{k}$$

We take the attractive case $Z_1 Z_2 < 0$, or $\lambda > 0$.

The gamma function has poles at zero and each negative integer. This gives us for the location of the poles

$$\ell + 1 + i\gamma = -n \qquad n = 0, 1, \ldots$$

$$\ell = -1 - n + \frac{i\lambda}{k}$$

We may plot in Fig. 4-5 the real and imaginary parts of ℓ as a function of k^2: the real part is pictured in solid lines and the imaginary part in dashed ones. We find of course the whole pattern of Fig. 4-1b.

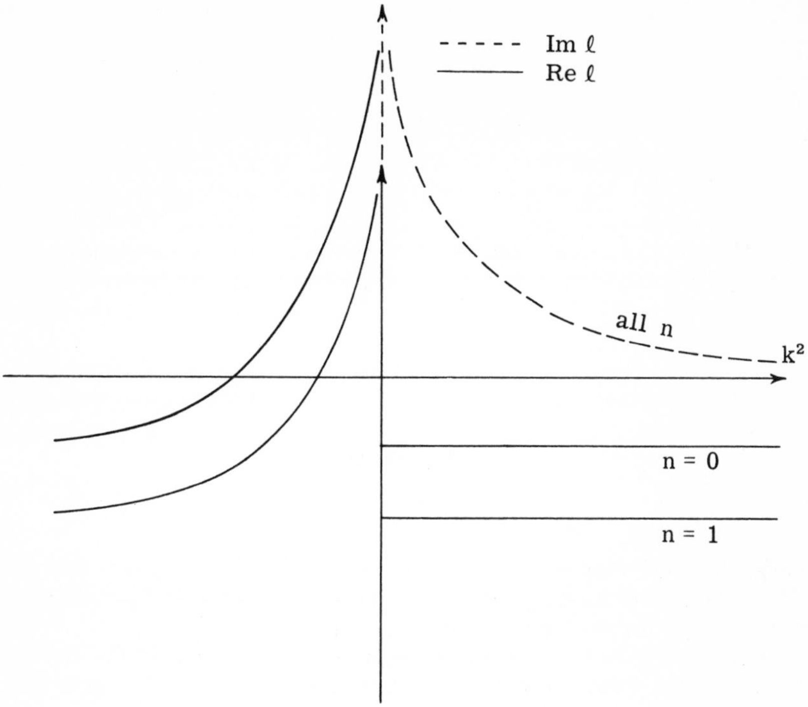

Figure 4-5

Another way of representing the trajectory is to plot it in the ℓ plane, giving the values of k^2 along the plot (see Fig. 4-6). But the Coulomb potential is also too singular: with its infinite range, it has an infinite number of bound states, and this causes the Regge poles to go to infinity. It is, however, a sad circumstance that none of the more realistic potentials is exactly solvable both for all energies and for all angular momenta. To get an idea of the real behavior of Regge poles in a more realistic situation, numerical computation had to be undertaken, and we take from the work of Ahmadzadeh, Burke, and Tate some of their results.

We have borrowed their results on a single attractive Yukawa potential, with a strength 2.8 times that necessary to bind an S state. We report in Fig. 4-7 the results for the leading four poles. The energies as indicated along the trajectory are in arbitrary units. We see that there is still only one bound state with this strength of the potential, at $\ell = 0$, $k^2 \sim -2$, owing to the first pole. The second pole passes quite near the value zero at zero energy, and probably causes what is usually called a "virtual state" in the S wave, that is, a large

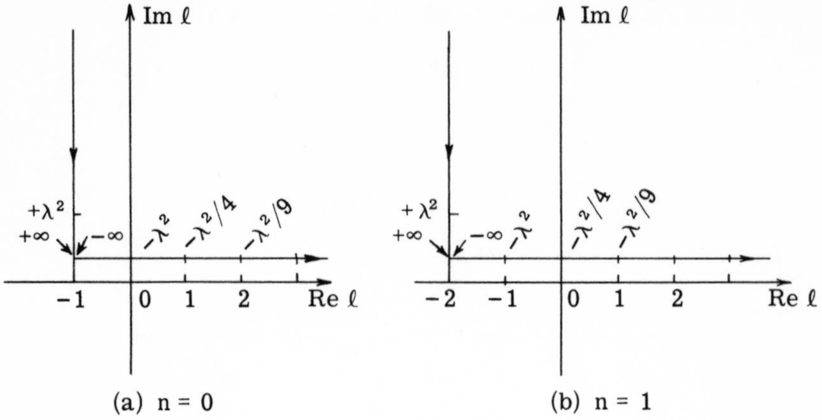

Figure 4-6

negative scattering length, in spite of the presence of the bound state. The potential is simply too strong and the bound state too far from zero energy for the usual pattern to hold.

The third pole has a behavior quite similar to that of the first two, but is too far away on the left to have any chance to show up in any physical connection. The behavior of the fourth pole, however, is strikingly different from that of the first three, and advises us to be cautious about generalizing too fast and guessing what a Regge pole behavior could be in a more general case. Of course, these trajectories for real k^2 describe a small part of the reality. We should, to be complete, analyze the values taken by the function $\alpha(k^2)$ for all values of k^2, real or complex, and on all sheets of the Riemann surface.

4-5 EXCHANGE FORCES—SIGNATURE

We mention briefly the case where there are exchange forces present, to introduce the concept of signature of a Regge pole. We have seen in Sec. 3-4 that the introduction of exchange forces can be practically shortcut by the splitting of the amplitude into its even and odd parts, which are the even and odd parts of amplitudes F^+ and F^-, referring to different potentials V^+ and V^-. The Regge poles of F^+ and F^- are then completely different in general. The Sommerfeld-Watson representation (4-3) takes the form

(a)

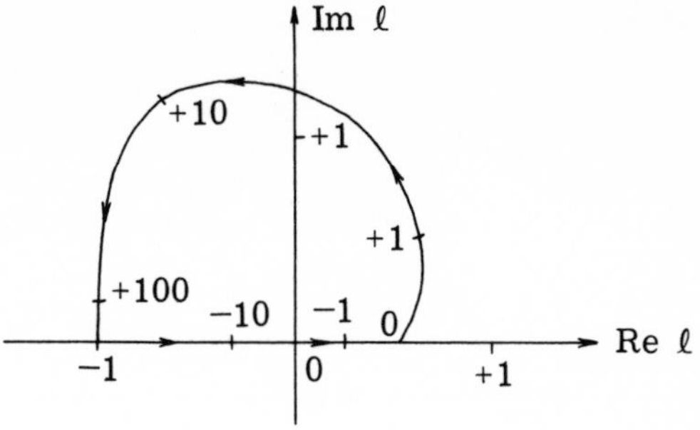

(b)

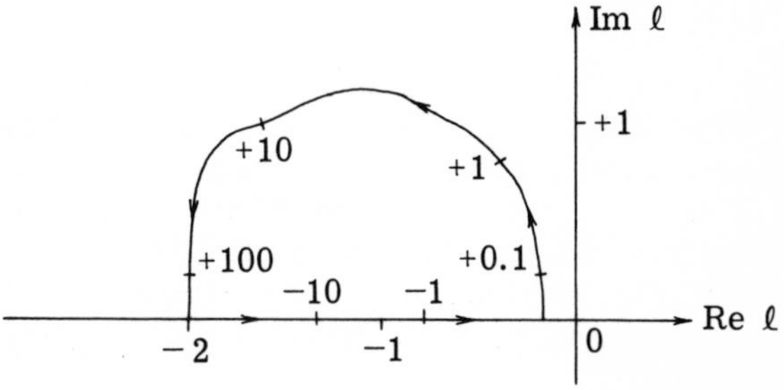

(c)

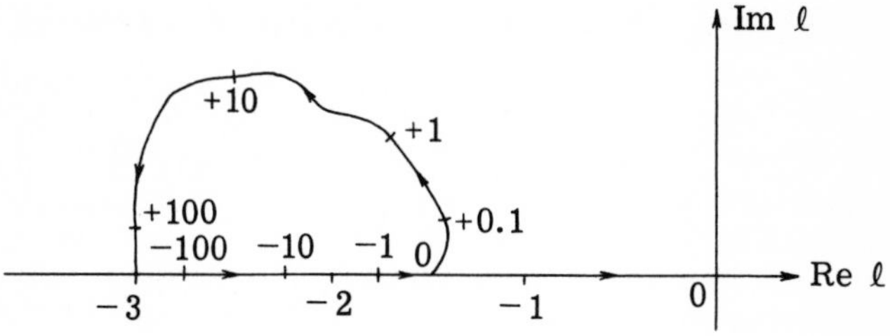

(d)

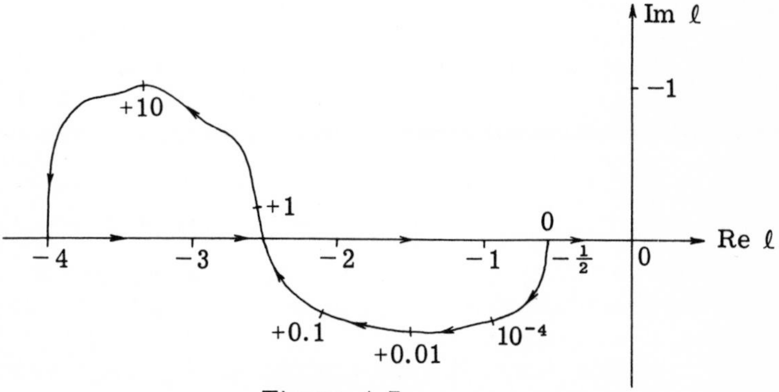

Figure 4-7

$$f(k^9, \cos\theta) = \int_{-1/2-i\infty}^{-1/2+i\infty} \frac{2\ell+1}{\sin \Pi\ell} \Big\{ a_\ell^+(k^2)\Big[P_\ell(-\cos\theta) + P_\ell(\cos\theta)\Big]$$

$$+ a_\ell^-(k^2)\Big[P_\ell(-\cos\theta) - P_\ell(\cos\theta)\Big]\Big\}\, d\ell$$

$$+ \sum_i \tfrac{1}{2}\beta_i^+(k^2)\Big[P_{\alpha_i^+(k^2)}(-\cos\theta) + P_{\alpha_i^+(k^2)}(\cos\theta)\Big]$$

$$+ \sum_j \tfrac{1}{2}\beta_j^-(k^2)\Big[P_{\alpha_j^-(k^2)}(-\cos\theta) - P_{\alpha_j^-(k^2)}(\cos\theta)\Big] \qquad (4\text{-}5)$$

It is to be noted that if one of the α^+ goes through an odd value ℓ, $\sin \Pi\ell$ vanishes, but $P_\ell(-\cos\theta) + P_\ell(\cos\theta)$ vanishes also, and the contribution of this pole is perfectly regular; the same phenomenon is true of the α^- going through an even integer value.

We may thus consider that the physical region for the α^+ is the even values only, and that for α^- the odd ones. We shall call *signature* the superscript $\pm$, which makes a distinction between the two kinds of poles.

4-6 ASYMPTOTIC BEHAVIOR IN MOMENTUM TRANSFER

A very peculiar feature of (4-3) and (4-5) is that they immediately give the asymptotic behavior of $f(k^2, \cos\theta)$ for large (unphysical) values of $\cos\theta$ or, what is the same, of $F(k^2,\Delta^2)$ for large values of Δ^2 for fixed k^2. This is due to the asymptotic behavior of $P_\ell(\cos\theta)$, which is, for large $\cos\theta$, essentially proportional to $(\cos\theta)^\ell$.

For complex ℓ, $|(\cos\theta)^\ell| = |\cos\theta|^{\mathrm{Re}\,\ell}\, e^{-\mathrm{Arg}(\cos\theta)\,\mathrm{Im}\,\ell}$. $\mathrm{Arg}(\cos\theta)$ denotes the phase of the complex number $\cos\theta$ ($\mathrm{Arg}\, x \equiv \mathrm{Im}\log x$). If $\cos\theta$ goes to infinity in some direction of the $\cos\theta$ plane, $\mathrm{Arg}(\cos\theta)$ stays fixed, and the asymptotic behavior essentially depends upon $|\cos\theta|^{\mathrm{Re}\,\ell}$. The dominant term will be that with the largest $\mathrm{Re}\,\ell$. Each P_ℓ in the integral of (4-3) has a $\mathrm{Re}\,\ell < 0$, and therefore the contribution of the integral goes to zero for large $\cos\theta$. The main term will come from the Regge pole contribution with the largest $\mathrm{Re}\,\alpha$. It corresponds to the Regge pole outmost on the right of Fig. 4-3, and finally we get an asymptotic behavior of the form

$$f(k^2, \cos\theta) \approx (\cos\theta)^{\alpha_1(k^2)} \qquad \text{for fixed } k^2 \text{ and large } \cos\theta \qquad (4\text{-}6)$$

or

$$F(k^2,\Delta^2) \approx (\Delta^2)^{\alpha_1(k^2)} \qquad \text{for fixed } k^2 \text{ and large } \Delta^2 \qquad (4\text{-}7)$$

We may make two remarks concerning this result.

First, it is very strange that, although for negative and large Δ^2 there are so many singularities of the amplitude, as mentioned in Sec. 3-3, they should add up to such a smooth asymptotic behavior as given by (4-7).

Second, this result is not interesting in any way as long as potential scattering only is concerned. It will take on its full meaning and physical implications only when we treat the relativistic S-matrix problem. This is due to the fact that large values of Δ^2 are far away from the physical region in potential scattering, and we shall see in Chapter 5 that this is in some sense not the case in the relativistic theory.

5

KINEMATICS OF RELATIVISTIC SCATTERING—CROSSING

5-1 KINEMATICS

Let us analyze the kinematics of a two-body reaction.

$$a_1 + a_2 \to a_1' + a_2'$$

We shall call $m_1 m_2 m_1' m_2'$ the masses of the particles a_1, a_2, a_1', a_2', which we shall suppose to be spinless, so that, as we have seen, the reaction will be completely described by a scattering amplitude which depends only on the kinetic energy and the scattering angle, as described in Chapter 1.

We shall call p_1, p_2, p_1', p_2' the four-momenta of these particles. As a result of energy-momentum conservation, these four-vectors satisfy the equality

$$p_1 + p_2 = p_1' + p_2' \tag{5-1}$$

One can choose to describe the reaction in any reference system. Some such systems which are frequently used are the laboratory system, where a_1 (or a_2) is at rest, or the center-of-mass system. However, the values of the kinetic energy and the scattering angle will depend on the choice of the reference system. To make a complete use of relativistic invariance, it will thus be useful to replace the system-dependent variables by invariant ones.

Let us see how we can define invariant variables. We shall first remark that there are only three independent four-vectors among p_1, p_2, p_1', p_2', so that it is sufficient to consider only p_1, p_2 and p_1', the last vector, p_2', being determined by the conservation relation (5-1). That equation may be given a simple geometrical meaning: Let us draw a vector AB in four-dimensional space equal to p_1 and BC equal to p_2; then if we draw the vector AD equal to p'_1, DC will be equal to p'_2 (Fig. 5-1a). Any change of reference system, i.e., any Lorentz transformation, will amount to a displacement of the tetrahedron ABCD in four-dimensional space. Up to these transformations, the tetrahedron will be completely determined by the squared length of its sides, i.e.,

$$p_1^2 = m_1^2 \qquad p_2^2 = m_2^2 \qquad p_1'^2 = m_1'^2 \qquad p_2'^2 = m_2'^2$$

and

$$s = AC^2 = (p_1 + p_2)^2 = (p'_1 + p'_2)^2$$

$$t = BD^2 = (p_1 - p'_1)^2 = (p_2 - p'_2)^2$$

As masses are obviously fixed quantities, we find that there are in fact only two independent invariant variables s and t, which we shall use in place of the system-dependent variables k^2 and $\cos\theta$.

Obviously, in place of drawing $AD = p'_1$, then $DC = p'_2$, we could as well draw another tetrahedron ABCD′ with $AD' = p'_2$ and $D'C = p'_1$ (Fig. 5-1b). There is no *a priori* reason to prefer one or the other, so that the other invariant variable

$$u = BD'^2 = (p_1 - p'_2)^2 = (p_2 - p'_1)^2$$

should be kept on the same footing as t. As there are only six independent invariant quantities, u has to be a function of s, t, m_1^2, m_2^2, $m_1'^2$, and $m_2'^2$.

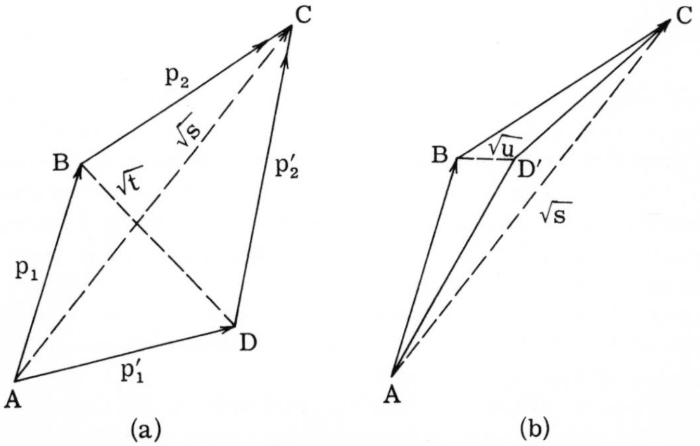

Figure 5-1

It follows easily from the conservation relation (5-1) that

$$s + t + u = m_1^2 + m_2^2 + m_1'^2 + m_2'^2 \tag{5-2}$$

These variables may be given a simple physical interpretation: in the center-of-mass system the three-dimensional momenta $\mathbf{p}_1$ and $\mathbf{p}_2$ are opposite, so that s reduces to the square of the total energy $(p_1^0 + p_2^0)^2$. When the masses m_1 and m_1', m_2 and m_2' are equal, as they are in elastic scattering, then the energies p_1^0 and $p_1'^0$, p_2^0 and $p_2'^0$ are equal, so that $-t$ reduces to Δ^2, the square of the momentum transfer, since

$$t = -(\mathbf{p}_1 - \mathbf{p}_1')^2 = -\Delta^2$$

Furthermore, when m_1 and m_2 are also equal, as is the case, for instance, for neutron-proton scattering, u may also be interpreted as minus the square of neutron-proton (charge-exchange) momentum transfer, while t is minus the square of proton-proton (elastic) momentum transfer. In the general case where masses are different, t and u keep their meaning as the invariant squares of *four-dimensional* momentum transfers.

We shall now stick for a while to neutron-proton scattering as an example. We shall neglect the small neutron-proton mass difference and the spins of the nucleons, treating them as spinless particles. The modifications introduced by the spins will be indicated later on.

Let us call k the center-of-mass momentum and θ the scattering angle. From the preceding interpretation of s,t,u, the relations between the two sets of variables read

$$\begin{aligned} s &= 4(k^2 + m^2) \\ t &= -2k^2(1 - \cos\theta) \\ u &= -2k^2(1 + \cos\theta) \end{aligned} \tag{5-3}$$

where m is the common proton and neutron mass.

In Chapter 3 it was found convenient to visualize the properties of the scattering amplitude as a function of k^2 and Δ^2 by drawing the region of physical k^2 and Δ^2 on a two-dimensional plot. Here, in place of these variables, we may use s and t. For a physical situation k is real and $\cos\theta$ lies between -1 and $+1$, i.e., s is larger than $4m^2$ and $0 > t > -4k^2$. This physical region is shown as the shaded area in Fig. 5-2.

In such a plot, a line u = constant will make a 45° angle with the two axes. To keep the symmetry between t and u it is convenient to use triangular coordinates. Such a coordinate system is obtained by

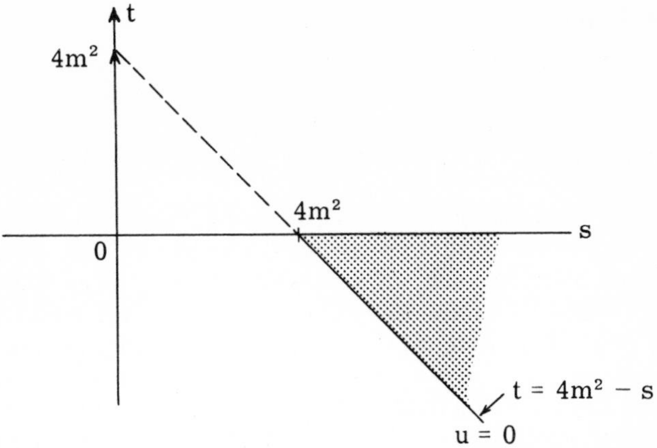

Figure 5-2

drawing three axes making equal (120°) angles (Fig. 5-3) and representing s, t, and u as the respective (oriented) distances of a point to these axes. The relation (5-2) will thus be automatically satisfied if the units are conveniently chosen.

This coordinate system is shown in Fig. 5-3 together with the physical region of p − n scattering, bounded by the two lines $\cos\theta = 1$, $\cos\theta = -1$, i.e., $t = 0$, $u = 0$.

Any point of the plane defines values of k^2 and $\cos\theta$ through (5-3). However, if this point is not in the shaded area, it will give either negative values of k^2 or values of $\cos\theta$ which do not lie between −1 and +1, or both. These values of k^2 and $\cos\theta$ clearly correspond to complex values of the c.m. momentum **k**.

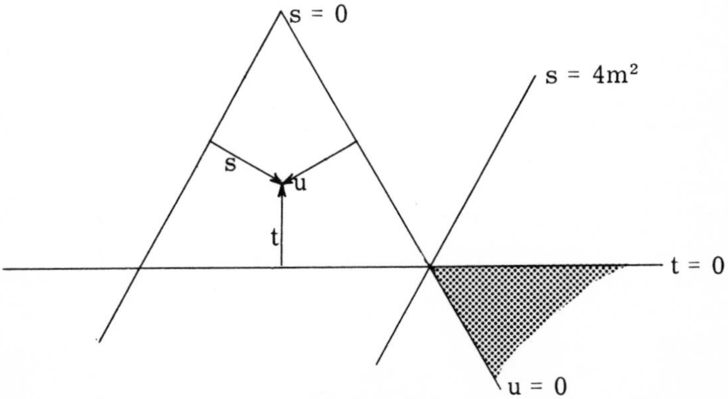

Figure 5-3

5-2 CROSSING

Scattering amplitudes have a certain symmetry with respect to the interchange of particles and antiparticles, which is known as crossing symmetry. We shall introduce it by recalling first how antiparticles come into physics. We start with an example borrowed from solid-state physics.

It is well known that the metallic atoms, when assembled in a crystal, lose some of their peripheral electrons. The crystal is thus formed by a regular array of ions while the electrons which have been pulled out from the atoms are submitted to the electrostatic potential of these ions. This potential has the same periodic properties as the crystal and in Fig. 5-4 we indicate how it appears in an ideal one-dimensional crystal. The dots on the x axis represent the ion positions.

For many applications, it is sufficient to approximate the periodic potential V(x) by an attractive constant mean potential $-U$ so that the "free" electrons will satisfy the simple Schrödinger equation

$$\left[-\frac{1}{2m}\nabla^2 - E + U\right]\Psi(x) = 0$$

There exist exponential solutions of that equation

$$\Psi(x) = e^{-i\mathbf{p}\cdot\mathbf{x}}$$

corresponding to a well-defined value $\mathbf{p}$ of the momentum and to an eigenvalue of the energy $E = (\mathbf{p}^2/2m) - U$. As required by the Pauli

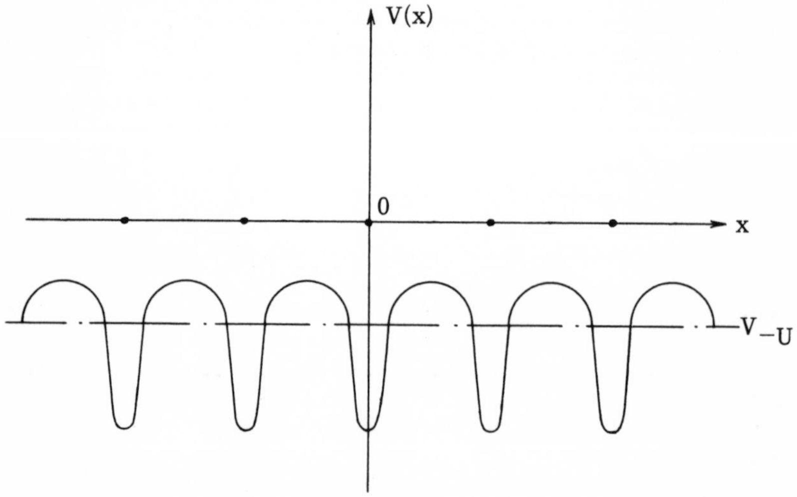

Figure 5-4

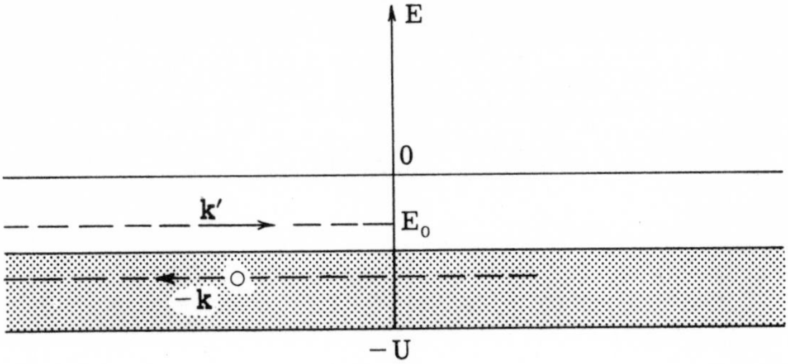

Figure 5-5

principle, no more than two electrons can have the same momentum, so that, at low temperatures, the electrons will fill up the lowest energy levels from the ground-state energy $-U$ up to some maximum energy E_0. These energy levels lie in the shaded region on Fig. 5-5 and they constitute the so-called "Fermi sea."

The complete Fermi sea has a total charge Q, a total energy $\mathcal{E}$, but a zero total momentum and zero total current, as the momenta and currents of the electrons balance each other in pairs. Electric or thermal conductivity is due to the excitation of the electrons from the Fermi sea: an excited electron jumps from its initial momentum $\mathbf{k}$ and initial energy $E = (k^2/2m) - U < E_0$ to a level higher than "Fermi sea level" E_0, with a momentum $\mathbf{k}'$ and an energy $E' = (\mathbf{k}'^2/2m) - U > E_0$. The remaining electrons now have a total charge $Q - e$, a total energy $\mathcal{E} - E$, and a total momentum $-\mathbf{k}$. We may consider that, instead of pulling an electron out of the Fermi sea, the excitation has pushed in a "hole" with charge $-e$, energy $-E = -(k^2/2m) + U$, and momentum $-\mathbf{k}$. Both the excited electrons and the holes can carry net charge or energy, that is, are responsible for transfers of electricity or heat.

Analogous considerations have been applied to the quasi-filled shells of atomic electrons. Here again, one may consider a shell where an electron is lacking as a complete shell plus a positive hole.

A very important application of this notion of "hole" has been made by Dirac in his theory of the positron. As is well known, the Dirac equation for the free electron allows negative as well as positive eigenvalues of the energy, so that an electron with momentum $\mathbf{k}$ can have an energy $E = \pm\sqrt{k^2 + m^2}$. The possible values of E thus range either from $-\infty$ to $-m$ or from $+m$ to $+\infty$, as shown in Fig. 5-6.

Clearly, the negative energy solutions have no direct physical meaning, but Dirac gave them one in the following way: suppose that

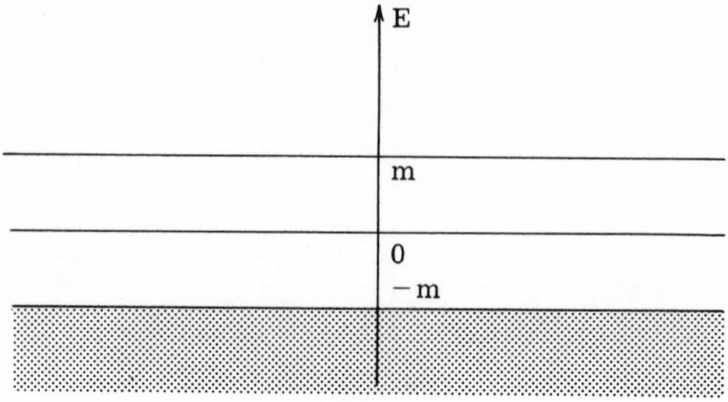

Figure 5-6

all negative energy states are filled up by electrons, thus making an abyssal Fermi sea. All these electrons will not give rise to observable effects since they all balance two by two in order to give total momentum, current, angular momentum, Coulomb field, and so on, equal to zero. We identify this state with the vacuum. The possible energy of any supernumerary electron will be positive, since Pauli's principle forbids it to occupy an already filled state with negative energy and so all observable electrons will have positive energies.

If an electron with negative energy is excited, it will necessarily get a positive energy, since all the states of the Fermi sea are forbidden by the Pauli principle. A hole will thus be created in the sea. Let us see what the observable effects of that hole will be.

First, the hole may again be considered as an object of minus the charge of the electron, since the total charge of the Fermi sea has diminished by one electron charge.

Second, the hole has a positive energy. Indeed, let us suppose that the negative energy electron has been excited from the top of the Fermi sea, energy $-m$, to the ground-state positive energy $+m$; it is then necessary to furnish it the gap energy $2m$. But, as the electron itself has finally the energy m, the hole must be considered also to have the positive energy m. In the same way a hole created at any energy level $-E$ may be considered as having an energy $+E$.

Finally, the hole has momentum $-\mathbf{k}$, if it has been created by suppression of an electron of momentum $\mathbf{k}$. Effectively, this electron was balanced by another electron with negative energy, momentum $-\mathbf{k}$. After excitation, the current $e\mathbf{v}$ of that second electron will become observable. But $\mathbf{v}$ is equal to the ratio of the momentum $-\mathbf{k}$ by the energy $-E$ of the electron, i.e., $\mathbf{v} = \mathbf{k}/E$. As the hole has positive energy, opposite charge, and must give the same current, its momentum is $-\mathbf{k}$.

Dirac called that hole the antiparticle of the electron or positron. It is thus completely equivalent in that theory to consider the effects of a positron with momentum **k**, positive energy E, or that of the balancing electron with momentum $-\mathbf{k}$, energy $-E$. One can also say that the electron of the Fermi sea with four-momentum $(-E,-\mathbf{k})$ and its "hole," the positron with four-momentum $(E,\mathbf{k})$, are together equivalent to nothing (the vacuum).

Let us see the consequences of that equivalence for scattering amplitudes. Consider again the reaction

$$\begin{array}{ccccccc} p & + & n & \rightarrow & p & + & n \\ p_1 & & p_2 & & p_1' & & p_2' \end{array} \tag{5-4}$$

where we have indicated the four-momenta of the particles. Such a scattering is customarily symbolized by a graph as in Fig. 5-7 and the corresponding scattering amplitude is $A^I(p_1,p_2,p_1',p_2')$.

Let us now suppose that in the initial state there is a pair of neutron $n(p_2')$ and antineutron $\bar{n}(-p_2')$ and that in the final state there is also a pair $n(p_2),\bar{n}(-p_2)$. From our earlier considerations, that does not amount to a real modification of these states. We thus get the reaction

$$\begin{array}{ccccccccccccccc} p & + & n & + & n & + & \bar{n} & \rightarrow & p & + & n & + & n & + & \bar{n} \\ p_1 & & p_2 & & p_2' & & -p_2' & & p_1' & & p_2' & & p_2 & & -p_2 \end{array}$$

As we find the same states of neutrons in the initial and final state, this is in fact nothing but the reaction

$$\begin{array}{ccccccc} p & + & \bar{n} & \rightarrow & p & + & \bar{n} \\ p_1 & & -p_2' & & p_1' & & -p_2 \end{array}$$

which must be closely related to reaction (5-4). We thus have a simple rule expressing the fact that in a reaction it is possible to replace a

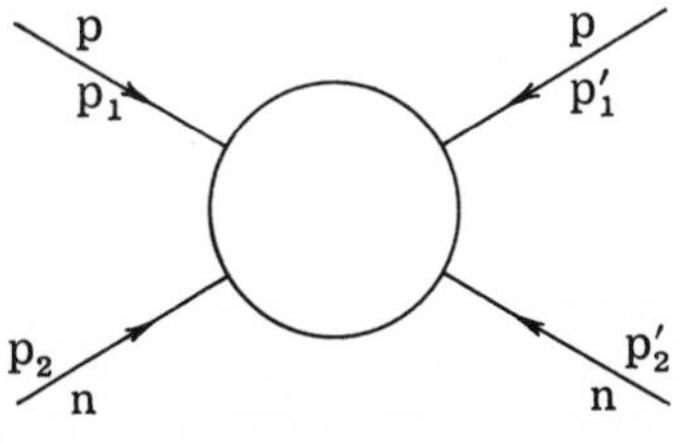

Figure 5-7

particle on one side of a reaction by its antiparticle with opposite four-momentum on the other side. This is the *crossing symmetry*.

What properties of collision amplitudes correspond to crossing symmetry? Clearly, if we introduce the amplitude $A^{II}(q_1 q_2 q_1' q_2')$ for the crossed reaction

$$\begin{matrix} p & + & \bar{n} & \rightarrow & p & + & \bar{n} \\ q_1 & & q_2 & & q_1' & & q_2' \end{matrix} \tag{5-5}$$

then

$$A^{I}(p_1 p_2 p_1' p_2') = A^{II}(p_1, -p_2', p_1', -p_2) \tag{5-6}$$

5-3 CROSSED REACTIONS

The crossing relation (5-6) is rather simple. However, we know what a collision amplitude is only for physical situations where, in particular, energies are positive, so that it is impossible that the two members of (5-6) correspond together to a physical situation: If, for instance, the energy of the neutron p_2^0 is positive, then the energy of the antineutron $q_2'^0 = -p_2^0$ is negative. As the description of physical situations (i.e., the "physical region") was quite clear on the (s,t,u) plot, it seems natural, in view of (5-6), to put the physical regions for crossed reactions on the same plot.

Let us call k_u the center-of-mass momentum of reaction (5-5) and θ_u the corresponding scattering angle; then in the same way as for reaction (5-4),

$$\begin{aligned} s &= (p_1 + p_2)^2 = (q_1 - q_2')^2 = -2k_u^2(1 + \cos\theta_u) \\ t &= (p_1 - p_1')^2 = (q_1 - q_1')^2 = -2k_u^2(1 - \cos\theta_u) \\ u &= (p_1 - p_2')^2 = (q_1 + q_2)^2 = 4(k_u^2 + m^2) \end{aligned} \tag{5-7}$$

The physical region for reaction (5-5) corresponds to the domain

$$k_u^2 > 0 \qquad -1 < \cos\theta_u < 1$$

i.e.,

$$u > 4m^2 \qquad t < 0 \qquad u < 0$$

and it is shown in Fig. 5-8 together with the physical region for reaction (5-4).

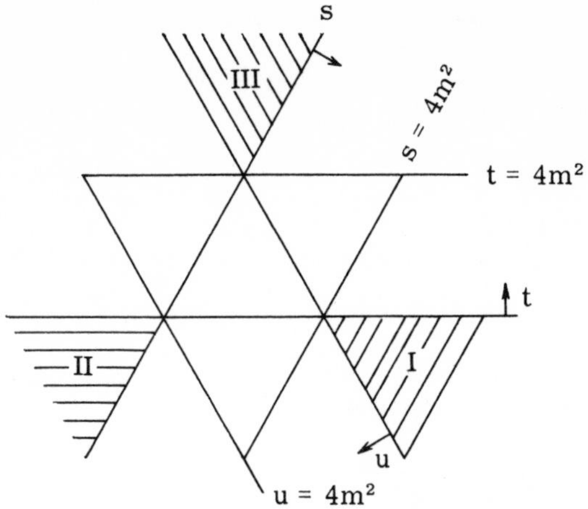

Figure 5-8

We have also plotted the physical region for the other crossed reaction

$$\begin{array}{cccc} p + \overline{p} & \rightarrow & \overline{n} + n \\ r_1 \quad r_2 & & r_1' \quad r_2 \end{array} \tag{5-8}$$

which satisfies

$$A^{I}(p_1 p_2 p_1' p_2') = A^{III}(p_1, -p_1', -p_2, +p_2') \tag{5-9}$$

If we call k_t the c.m. momentum for reaction (5-8) and θ_t the scattering angle, then writing $p_1 = r_1$, $-p_1' = r_2$, $-p_2 = r_1'$, $p_2' = r_2'$, one has

$$\begin{aligned} s &= (p_1 + p_2) = (r_1 - r_1')^2 = -2k_t^2(1 - \cos\theta_t) \\ t &= (p_1 - p_1')^2 = (r_1 + r_2)^2 = 4(k_t^2 + m^2) \\ u &= (p_1 - p_2')^2 = (r_1 - r_2')^2 = -2k_t^2(1 + \cos\theta_t) \end{aligned} \tag{5-10}$$

so that the physical region (5-8) is defined by $t > 4m^2$, $s < 0$, $u < 0$.

We list here the complete set of reactions which may be derived from $p - n$ scattering by repeated crossing:

$$\begin{array}{ll} p + n \rightarrow p + n & \overline{p} + \overline{n} \rightarrow \overline{p} + \overline{n} \\ p + \overline{n} \rightarrow p + \overline{n} & p + \overline{p} \rightarrow n + \overline{n} \\ \overline{p} + n \rightarrow \overline{p} + n & n + \overline{n} \rightarrow p + \overline{p} \end{array}$$

In general, one may link the amplitudes for twelve different reactions by crossing symmetry and time-reversal invariance. Remember that the latter just expresses that the amplitudes for two inverse reactions like, for instance,

$$\pi + p \rightarrow \Lambda + K$$

and

$$\Lambda + K \rightarrow \pi + p$$

just differ by kinematical and spin factors. In that example, we can say that the amplitudes for the twelve reactions

$\pi^- + p \rightarrow \Lambda + K^0$	$K^0 + \Lambda \rightarrow \pi^- + p$	$\pi^+ + \bar{p} \rightarrow \bar{\Lambda} + \bar{K}^0$
$\bar{K}^0 + \bar{\Lambda} \rightarrow \pi^+ + \bar{p}$	$\bar{K}^0 + p \rightarrow \Lambda + \pi^+$	$\pi^+ + \Lambda \rightarrow \bar{K}^0 + p$
$K^0 + \bar{p} \rightarrow \bar{\Lambda} + \pi^-$	$\pi^- + \bar{\Lambda} \rightarrow K^0 + \bar{p}$	$\pi^- + \bar{K}^0 \rightarrow \Lambda + \bar{p}$
$\Lambda + \bar{p} \rightarrow \pi^- + \bar{K}^0$	$\pi^+ + K^0 \rightarrow \bar{\Lambda} + p$	$\bar{\Lambda} + p \rightarrow \pi^+ + K^0$

are all related by crossing or time reversal.

Inverse reactions as well as charge-conjugate reactions have the same physical regions, but this is well known and we shall not insist on them any more.

The crossing relations (5-6) and (5-9) tell us that essentially the same function A(s,t,u) constitutes the amplitude for the three crossed reactions (5-4), (5-5), and (5-8). We shall see later on what one has to understand by the "same" function. Beforehand we shall examine the (s,t,u) plot of the physical regions of crossed reactions in the general case.

5-4 KINEMATICS OF CROSSED REACTIONS

Consider a general reaction

$$a_1 + a_2 \rightarrow a_3 + a_4 \qquad (5\text{-}11)$$

As crossing will lead us to introduce negative energies, it is simpler to consider, in a graph analogous to that of Fig. 5-7, that all particles are ingoing (see Fig. 5-9), so that we shall call $p_1, p_2, -p_3, -p_4$ the four-momenta of a_1, a_2, a_3, a_4, these vectors satisfying the conservation relation

$$p_1 + p_2 + p_3 + p_4 = 0$$

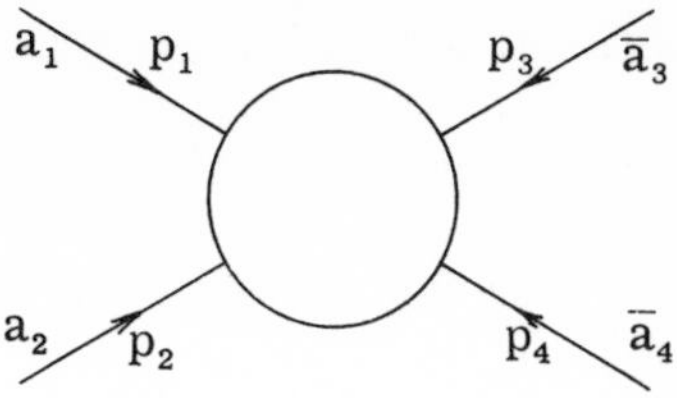

Figure 5-9

With this new notation, we shall have

$$p_1^2 = m_1^2 \qquad p_2^2 = m_2^2 \qquad p_3^2 = m_3^2 \qquad p_4^2 = m_4^2$$

$$\begin{aligned} s &= (p_1 + p_2)^2 = (p_3 + p_4)^2 \\ t &= (p_1 + p_3)^2 = (p_2 + p_4)^2 \\ u &= (p_1 + p_4)^2 = (p_2 + p_3)^2 \end{aligned} \tag{5-12}$$

$$s + t + u = m_1^2 + m_2^2 + m_3^2 + m_4^2 \tag{5-13}$$

The boundary of the physical region is more complicated in the case of four arbitrary masses, just as the whole kinematics is. However one finds that the three physical regions are limited by three branches of a certain third-order algebraic curve (C). It is fairly easy to draw approximately this curve (C) by the following very simple rules:

1. Draw the three axes $s = 0$, $t = 0$, $u = 0$ (the height of the triangle represents $m_1^2 + m_2^2 + m_3^2 + m_4^2$). These axes are the asymptotes, which cut (C) each at one point at most.

2. Draw the 12 lines

$$s = (m_1 \pm m_2)^2 \qquad s = (m_3 \pm m_4)^2$$

$$t = (m_1 \pm m_3)^2 \qquad t = (m_2 \pm m_4)^2$$

$$u = (m_1 \pm m_4)^2 \qquad u = (m_2 \pm m_3)^2$$

All these are tangent to (C) and do not cross it, unless they coincide, in which case they pass only through a double point, at which (C) crosses itself (all $m \neq 0$). Through each double point there are three pairs of coincident lines.

3. Now it should be fairly easy to have an idea of the shape of the curve, which has three infinite branches and a central blob. One can show that the branch with the lowest threshold cuts each of its asymptotes, the branch with the highest one, and the third branch one. These three points are on a straight line.

4. If there are two double points, (C) decomposes into a hyperbola and a straight line.

5. If there are three double points, (C) decomposes into three straight lines (Fig. 5-8).

6. Check: No straightline cuts (C) including the center blob in more than three points.

5-5 FIRST EXAMPLE: p — n SCATTERING

Let us redetermine the physical region for neutron-proton according to these rules. Here again, we neglect the proton-neutron mass difference.

All 12 tangents coincide two by two, and there are three double points, i.e., (C) decomposes into the three straight lines $s = 0$, $t = 0$, $u = 0$ (see Fig. 5-8).

5-6 SECOND EXAMPLE: PION-NUCLEON SCATTERING

According to the rules, we draw a triangle of height $2m^2 + 2\mu^2$ (Fig. 5-10) whose sides are the axes $s = 0$, $t = 0$, $u = 0$.

We choose to call the nucleons particles 1 and 3 and the pions 2 and 4.

The tangents parallel to $s = 0$ are $s = (m \pm \mu)^2$ twice. We have thus at least two double points.

The crossed reaction in u is again, interchanging the pions 2 and 4, the same, and we get $u = (m \pm \mu)^2$ twice.

Finally, the third reaction is

$$\begin{array}{cccc} N + & \overline{N} \rightarrow & \pi + & \pi \\ 1 & 3 & 2 & 4 \end{array}$$

The tangents are $t = 0$, twice, $t = (2\mu)^2$ and $t = (2m)^2$.

The double points are on the line $t = 0$ at $s = (m \pm \mu)^2, u(m \mp \mu)^2$.

The curve decomposes into the line $t = 0$ itself, and a hyperbola with the remaining asymptotes $s = 0$ and $u = 0$, passing through the double points and tangent to $t = 4\mu^2$ and $t = 4m^2$.

The center blob is formed by the arc ADB and the segment AB.

5-7 THIRD EXAMPLE: $K\mu_3$ DECAY AND DALITZ PLOT

Let us now consider the three-body decay of the K meson,

$$\begin{array}{cccc} K \rightarrow & \pi + & \mu + & \overline{\nu} \\ p_1 & p_3 & p_4 & p_2 \end{array} \qquad (5\text{-}14)$$

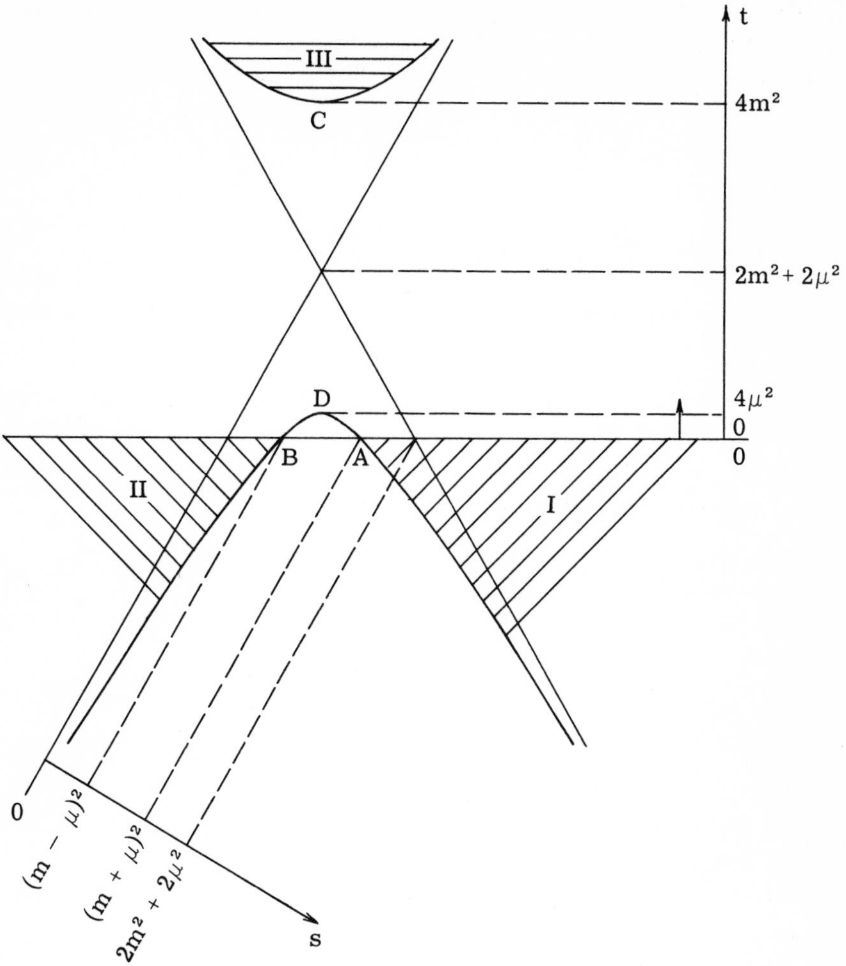

Figure 5-10

Reaction (5-14) is in fact due to weak interactions. However, as we are here interested only in kinematical considerations, there is no reason not to consider it. Together with (5-11) we shall consider the three crossed reactions

$$K + \overline{\mu} \rightarrow \pi + \overline{\nu} \qquad (\text{energy } \sqrt{u}) \tag{5-15}$$

$$K + \nu \rightarrow \pi + \mu \qquad (\text{energy } \sqrt{s}) \tag{5-16}$$

$$K + \pi \rightarrow \mu + \overline{\nu} \qquad (\text{energy } \sqrt{t}) \tag{5-17}$$

and we shall denote the masses by the same symbols as the particles, except for the neutrino, which has zero mass.

The physical region is now a true cubic curve with the tangents

$$u = (K + \mu)^2;\ (K - \mu)^2;\ \pi^2 \text{ twice}$$

$$s = (\pi + \mu)^2;\ (\pi - \mu)^2;\ K^2 \text{ twice}$$

$$t = (K + \pi)^2;\ (K - \pi)^2;\ \mu^2 \text{ twice}$$

The three double tangents intersect at a double point A and it is easy to draw the curve (C) (Fig. 5-11).

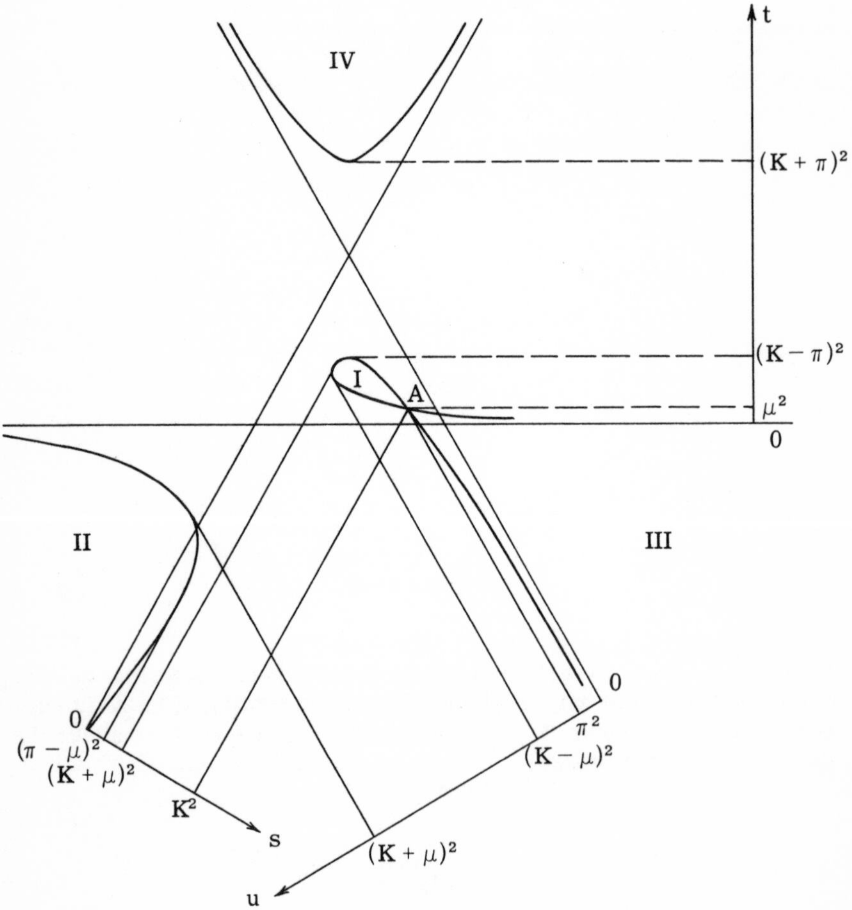

Figure 5-11

Why there is a double point is easy to see: in reaction (5-16) the threshold corresponds to a situation where the K meson is at rest and the incoming neutrino has zero energy and momentum. But that is kinematically indistinguishable from the situation where K decays, emitting a neutrino with zero energy. Consequently the physical region for the decay (5-14) is the loop which touches the physical region for reaction (5-16) at the double point.

The loop in Fig. 5-11 is generally called the Dalitz plot. It represents the set of values of s, t, and u allowed in the decay. In the K-meson rest system, the four-vector $p_1 = (m_1, 0)$ is fixed and, for instance,

$$s = (p_1 + p_2)^2 = (m_1 + E_2)^2 - \mathbf{p}_2^2 = m_1^2 + m_2^2 + 2m_1 E_2$$

so that s is, up to a constant, proportional to the c.m. energy E_2 of the second particle; in the same way u and t are proportional to E_1 and E_3. The plot of a decay rate in triangular coordinates E_1, E_2, E_3 is the Dalitz plot. Its boundary is clearly given by the loop (5-14) in the case of $K\mu_3$ decay.

In a decay which does not result in any mass zero particle, there is still a loop as is shown by Fig. 5-12 for the K decay,

$$K \rightarrow \pi + \pi + \pi$$

However, it should be stressed that the loop has the meaning of a decay physical region only when one of the particles can decay into the three others. In general, there is always such a loop in any (s,t,u) plot, for instance the central triangle in Fig. 5-8 or the loop ABD in Fig. 5-12. Another example is shown in Sec. 5-8.

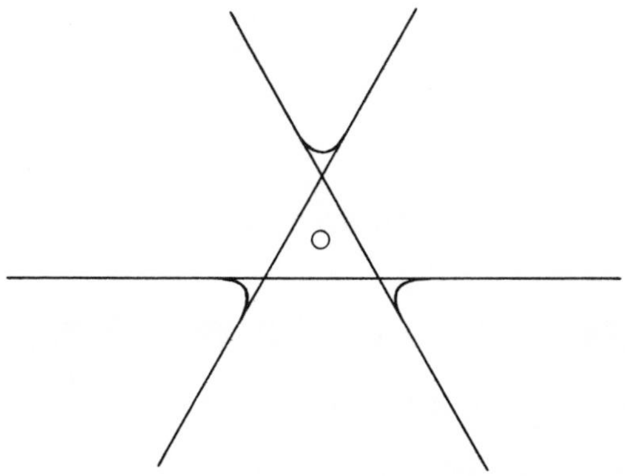

Figure 5-12

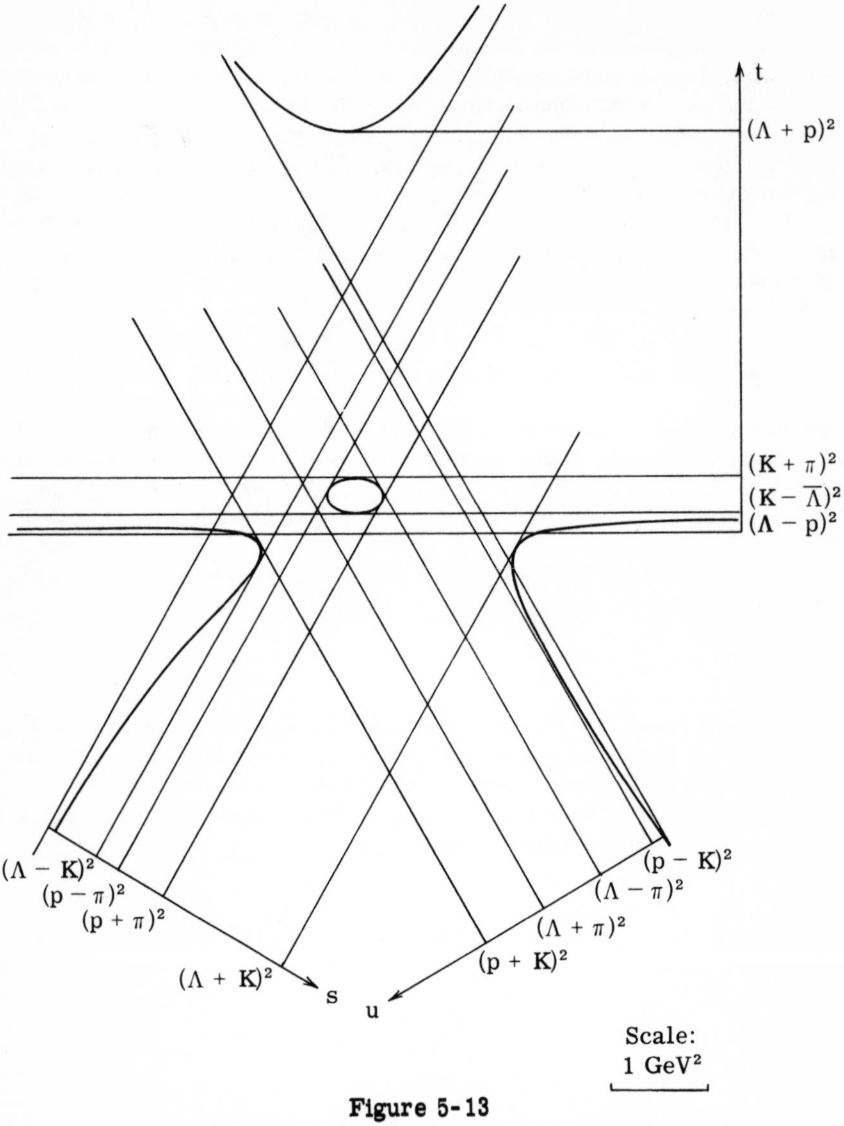

Figure 5-13

5-8 A GENERAL CASE: ASSOCIATED PRODUCTION

We give here for completeness the case of associated production

$$\pi + p \rightarrow \Lambda + K \tag{5-18}$$

together with its crossed reactions

$$p + \overline{K} \rightarrow \Lambda + \pi \tag{5-19}$$

$$p + \overline{\Lambda} \rightarrow \pi + K \tag{5-20}$$

where all masses are different and different from zero (Fig. 5-13).

6

RELATIVISTIC SCATTERING THEORY "À LA MANDELSTAM"

6-1 FORMULATION OF THE PROBLEM

As we have seen in Chapter 5, a single function A(s,t,u) defines the amplitudes for several crossed reactions. What is, however, the meaning of that function?

A priori, when we consider for instance the reaction

$$\begin{array}{llll} p + n \rightarrow p + n & \text{energy } \sqrt{s} \\ p_1 \quad p_2 \quad -p_3 \quad -p_4 & \end{array} \qquad (6\text{-}1)$$

the scattering amplitude $f(k^2,\Delta^2)$, which may be considered as a function of s,t,u, has a direct interpretation for physical situations only, i.e., when s,t,u are in the physical region I (see Fig. 6-1).

In order to know what the scattering amplitude means for other values of the parameters, it is necessary to have some mathematical way of defining it. In nonrelativistic theory this mathematical extension was afforded by the Schrödinger equation, which we could still write for nonphysical values of k^2. We were able to define $f(k^2,\Delta^2)$ through the integral form of the Schrödinger equation, and it made sense for nonphysical values of Δ^2. In that way, it was possible to define $f(k^2,\Delta^2)$ even for complex values of k^2 and Δ^2 and to show that it was an analytic function of these two variables.

We should be quite happy if we could prove in the relativistic case that $f(k^2,\Delta^2)$ is an analytic function, since that would provide a way to pass, by analytic continuation, from the physical region I to the physical regions II and III. The meaning of crossing symmetry would then be merely: *a single analytic function of s,t,u defines the amplitudes of crossed reactions*.

Actually, one is very far from proving such a strong analyticity

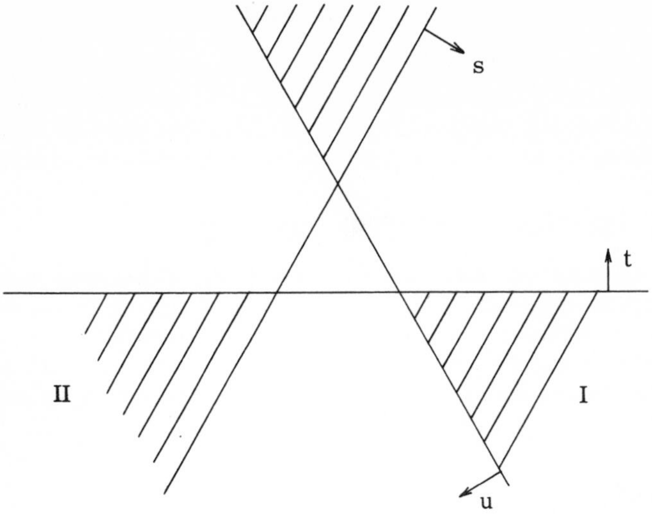

Figure 6-1

property. The most ambitious way to attack the problem would be to derive the analyticity of $f(k^2,\Delta^2)$ from the most general axioms of quantum field theory, i.e., just from the assumption that there exist fields giving a meaning to scattering theory and to the existing particles. Using this method it has been possible to show that $f(k^2,\Delta^2)$ is an analytic function of k^2 and Δ^2 in some neighborhood of the physical regions, but one is very far from justifying the extension of the same amplitude from a physical region to another one.

Another method has been tried: Specify the field theory by a Hamiltonian and compute the scattering amplitude through perturbation theory, i.e., the analogue of the nonrelativistic Born series. This method could be arranged into a proof if one could show:

1. That all orders of perturbation theory give analytic contributions to the scattering amplitude.
2. That renormalization does not give troubles.
3. That the perturbation series converges.
4. That the sum of this series has the same analytic properties as all its terms.

In fact, it is easy to dispose of point 2 (renormalization). However, it has been up to now impossible to find what domain of analyticity is obtained in point 1. Complete investigations have been made only of the first few orders in perturbation theory. As for point 3, there is every reason to believe that it is wrong, which leaves no sense to point 4. We have indeed seen in Chapter 3 that the appearance of bound states or resonances must correspond to some divergence of the series.

Consequently, all the considerations we shall make are only hypotheses consistent with the first few orders of perturbation theory.

We shall now try to see what are, just from the physical viewpoint, the most natural analyticity hypotheses for the scattering amplitudes.

6-2 THE INVARIANT SCATTERING AMPLITUDE

As we have already said, we neglect the spin of particles unless the contrary is explicitly stated. Our first task will be to specify what scattering amplitude is in fact the same for all crossed reactions. The meaning of that question is the following: we have already introduced a scattering amplitude for reaction I, $f^I(k^2, \cos\theta)$, which we shall write $f^I(s,t,u)$ such that

$$\frac{d\sigma^I}{d\Omega^I} = |f^I|^2$$

In the same way, there exists another amplitude $f^{II}(s,t,u)$ for the crossed reaction II.

$$p + \overline{n} \rightarrow p + \overline{n} \qquad \text{energy } \sqrt{u}$$

with (6-2)

$$\frac{d\sigma^{II}}{d\Omega^{II}} = |f^{II}|^2$$

But, in place of f^I, one could as well use another amplitude, proportional to the first one, such as, for instance,

$$g^I = \frac{1}{\sqrt{2k^2}} f^I$$

Since $t = -2k^2(1 - \cos\theta)$ one has

$$|g^I|^2 = \frac{1}{2k^2}|f^I|^2 = \frac{1}{2k^2}\frac{d\sigma}{d\Omega} = \frac{1}{2\pi}\frac{1}{2k^2}\frac{d\sigma}{d\cos\theta} = \frac{1}{2\pi}\frac{d\sigma}{dt}$$

and there is no *a priori* reason for $d\sigma/d\Omega$ to be more fundamental than $d\sigma/dt$. One can also define

$$g^{II} = \frac{1}{\sqrt{2q^2}} f^{II}$$

Now, it is impossible to have together the crossing relations

$$f^{I}(s,t,u) = f^{II}(u,t,s) \tag{6-3}$$

and

$$g^{I}(s,t,u) = g^{II}(u,t,s)$$

since the first relation gives

$$\sqrt{s - 4m^2}\, g^{I} = \sqrt{u - 4m^2}\, g^{II} \tag{6-4}$$

which contradicts the second one, and, generally, there are few forms of the amplitude for which crossing has the simple form (6-3). The field-theoretical invariant amplitude (which is obtained by taking S-matrix elements between states with Lorentz-invariant normalization) turns out to satisfy these requirements, and is

$$A(s,t,u) = \sqrt{s}\, f(k^2,\Delta^2) \tag{6-5}$$

It may be verified from perturbation theory that the function A(s,t,u) satisfies actually the crossing relations in their simple form (6-3), i.e.,

$$\sqrt{s}\, f^{I}(k_{I}^{2},\Delta_{I}^{2}) = \sqrt{u}\, f^{II}(k_{II}^{2},\Delta_{II}^{2})$$

Perturbation theory shows that this invariant function A(s,t,u) has the simplest analytical properties among all possible reaction amplitudes which could differ by the normalization of states. It is that amplitude that we shall consider more specifically in the future.

6-3 THE NONRELATIVISTIC REGION

Let us now come back to proton-neutron scattering. For small-enough values of the energy, it must be possible to describe it in a nonrelativistic manner, i.e., to write for the wave function an ordinary Schrödinger equation. It is not *a priori* quite obvious that one can use in that equation an ordinary local potential. However there is by now fairly good experimental evidence that, if the effects of spin are neglected, the interaction can be described by a combination of a local (direct) potential and an exchange potential. Although the spin effects are by no means negligible, we shall ignore them for the purposes of this discussion.

Let us now suppose that these potentials are not too singular. More precisely, let us suppose that they can be written as superpositions of Yukawa potentials:

$$V(r) = \int_a^\infty \frac{e^{-\mu r}}{r} \pi(\mu)\, d\mu$$

That class of potentials is in fact very large, and the experimentally determined V(r) can indeed be given that form.

All properties of the scattering amplitude which have been established from the Schrödinger equation must then be satisfied by the full scattering amplitude as long as the nonrelativistic approximation is correct, i.e., as long as the momenta are small compared with the nucleon mass m. This means that the square of the c.m. momentum k^2 is small as compared to m^2 and the momentum transfer t is also much smaller than m^2. As one has $s = 4(k^2 + m^2)$ and $t = -\Delta^2$, we know thus that for a region of the (s,t,u) plot broadly indicated by a circle in Fig. 6-1, A(s,t,u) is an analytic function of s and t (i.e., of s, t, and u) and that it has only the singularities which we have determined, i.e.:

1. A(s,t,u) has a pole in s corresponding to the existence of the deuteron which is a proton-neutron bound state. In Chapter 3 we have shown that this pole occurs at $k^2 = -B$, where B is the deuteron binding energy. However, we had chosen a system of units where the reduced mass of the p − n system was taken as $\frac{1}{2}$. This reduced mass is in fact $m_p m_n/(m_p + m_n) = m/2$, i.e., the pole occurs at $k^2 = -mB$ or at $s = 4(k^2 + m^2) = 4m(m - B)$. If we neglect B/m, as is indeed allowed in a nonrelativistic limit, $4m(m - B) \simeq (2m - B)^2$ and 2m − B is nothing but the deuteron mass M, so that the pole occurs very near M^2.

However, it was shown in Chapter 2 that the deuteron pole appeared because the deuteron was a bound state of the p − n system (Fig. 6-2). This simple physical property must certainly be preserved in a relativistic theory, so that we shall now consider that the pole occurs when the total c.m. mass of the proton-neutron system $\sqrt{s}$ is equal to the deuteron mass, i.e., exactly for $s = M^2$.

2. A(s,t,u) has a cut starting from $k^2 = 0$, i.e., $s = 4m^2$. This cut appears when energy is large enough for scattering to become possible. It will certainly also remain in the relativistic theory.

3. A(s,t,u) has a cut for t real positive. In fact, it may even have a pole and a cut if, in the direct potential $V_1(r)$, there is an isolated Yukawa potential of range r_0, so that

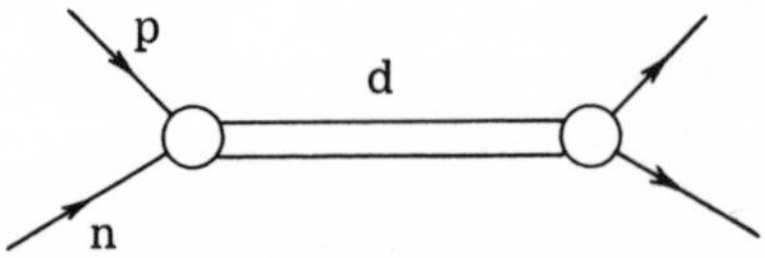

Figure 6-2

$$V_1(r) = V_0 \frac{e^{-r/r_0}}{r} + \int_b^\infty \frac{e^{-\mu r}}{r} \sigma'(\mu)\, d\mu$$

if $b > r_0^{-1}$, A(s,t,u) has a pole at $t = r_0^{-2}$ and a cut starting from $t = b^2$. As we have already shown, the position of these poles or cuts are related to the range of the direct potential.

4. In the same way, A(s,t,u) has a cut for u real positive and perhaps a pole. These singularities are introduced by the exchange potential $V_2(r)$ and their position is related to the range of that potential (remember that u is the square of the p − n momentum transfer).

It results from the analysis that the poles and cuts in s have positions which are completely defined by the masses of particles entering in the p − n processes while the position of the t and u poles and cuts are determined by ranges. We shall stick for a moment to the energy cuts. This will in fact allow us, after using crossing symmetry, to redetermine the momentum-transfer cuts together with a more precise determination of their position.

6-4 ANOTHER ENERGY CUT

In our treatment of potential scattering, no processes other than elastic scattering were taken into account. However, for large-enough energies, inelastic processes will appear, the first ones being pion production like

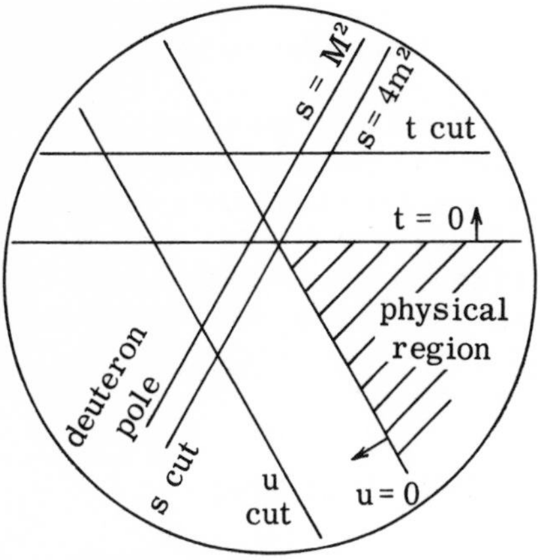

Figure 6-3
Relativistic kinematics.

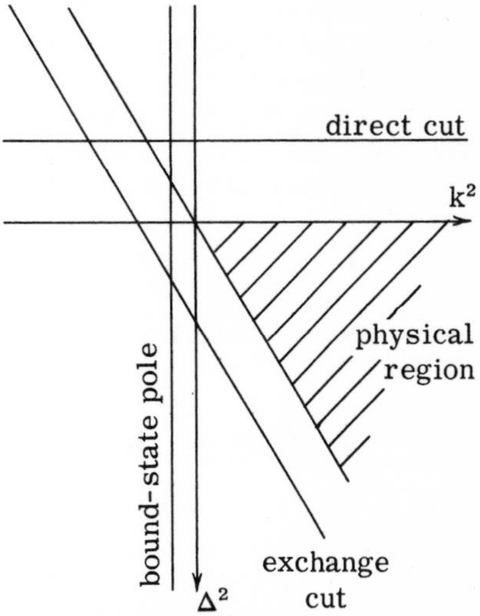

Figure 6-4
Nonrelativistic kinematics.

$$p + n \to p + n + \pi^0$$

$$\to n + n + \pi^+$$

$$\to p + p + \pi^-$$

They will take place as soon as the total c.m. energy $\sqrt{s}$ of the $p - n$ system is larger than the mass of the final states $2m + \mu$. (Here, we again call μ the pion mass, neglecting the small mass difference between neutral and charged pions.) One may wonder if this new process will affect the analytic properties of $A(s,t,u)$.

A simple argument shows that this must indeed be the case: there exist certain relations (unitarity relations), which we need not write here, and which express the fact that, below the inelastic threshold, all incoming particles are found in the final state, either scattered or transmitted without scattering. These relations are true for all real values of s between $4m^2$ and $(2m + \mu)^2$, If the amplitude was analytic, as a function of s, beyond $s = (2m + \mu)^2$, these relations would hold also beyond $(2m + \mu)^2$, and we would know that no inelastic process can take place, as no incident particle would be available for it. A singularity must therefore exist at $s = (2m + \mu)^2$, and it is linked with the opening of the $2N + \pi$ channel.

An analogous argument would lead us to assume the existence of a singularity of the amplitude at each value of the energy corresponding to a new channel, that is, at each threshold.

We can explain by an extension of this rule the appearance of the deuteron pole: it corresponds to a "virtual reaction" of two nucleons giving a deuteron, and hence gives a "threshold" singularity at the corresponding energy.

We are led in this way to generalize the above rule to all thresholds, real or virtual, that is, with an energy larger or smaller than the sum of the masses of the particles under consideration. Each threshold will be considered as the location of a singularity in the energy variable. A particular case of this rule is the appearance of a singularity at the ordinary elastic threshold ($s = 4m^2$ in the nucleon-nucleon case), which we met already in the case of potential scattering.

6-5 AN EXAMPLE: PROTON-ANTINEUTRON SCATTERING

Let us see how the preceding rule applies to the case of proton-antineutron scattering. We shall have to review all the possible one-energy states and all the possible final channels. As in Chapter 5, we shall call u the c.m. energy of the $p - \bar{n}$ system, and we shall call $A(s,t,u)$ the scattering amplitude since, by crossing, it must be the same as the proton-neutron amplitude.

The only one-particle state having the same quantum numbers as the $p-\bar{n}$ system is the π^+ meson, and we thus expect that A(s,t,u) has a pole at $u = p^2$.

Then comes the $\pi^+\pi^0$ channel, which opens for $u = (2\mu)^2$. Here it is clear that the reaction

$$p + \bar{n} \to \pi^+\pi^0$$

does not have a real meaning for $u \sim (2\mu)^2$. However, there will still be a singularity at $u = (2\mu)^2$, and a cut extending from $4\mu^2$ to $+\infty$.

Then there will be a singularity, on the cut, at $u = (3\mu)^2$, where the three-pion channel opens and another at $(4\mu)^2$ for four-pion channels, and so on.... There will also be singularities corresponding to the opening of the $K - \bar{K}$, $K - \bar{K} - \pi$ channels..., and so on and so forth until one arrives at $u = (2m)^2$, where the $p-\bar{n}$ channel will enter into play and give rise to a new singularity, which we shall call the "elastic" singularity. Afterward we shall have singularities for $N - \bar{N} - \pi$, $N\bar{N}\pi$, ...

These singularities (or at least the most important, i.e., the π pole, the 2π cut, and the $N\bar{N}$ cut) are shown in Fig. 6-5. The orientation of the physical region has been chosen here as in Fig. 6-1. The analogous plot for the $p\bar{p} \to n\bar{n}$ reaction is given in Fig. 6-6. Here there is also a pole given by the π^0, then a 2π cut, and so on.

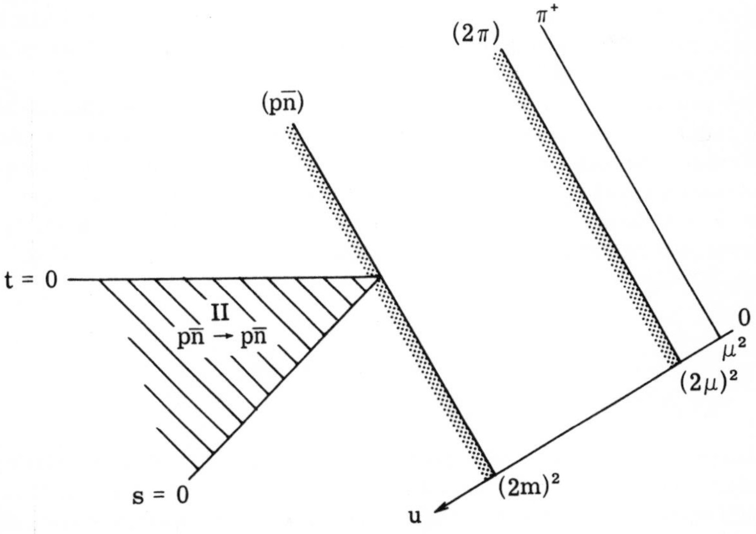

Figure 6-5

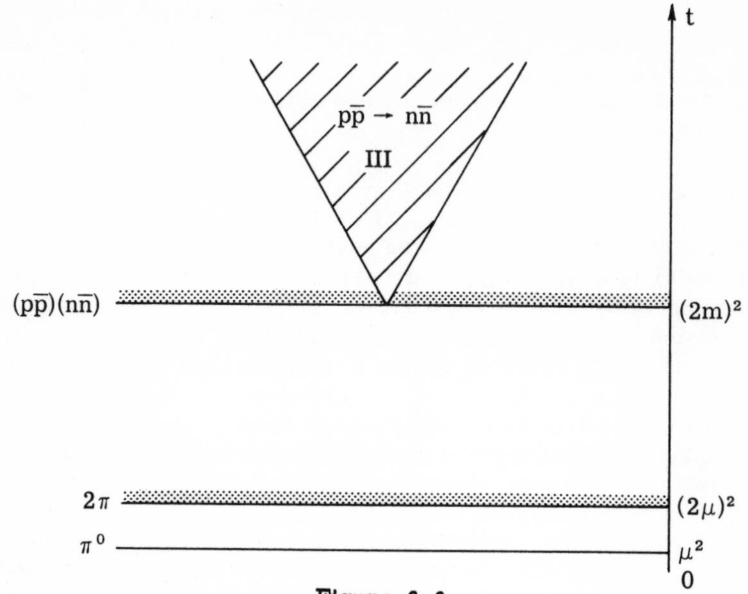

Figure 6-6

6-6 THE MANDELSTAM HYPOTHESIS

Mandelstam has proposed the following very simple hypothesis: A(s,t,u) is an analytic function of s, t, and u. Its sole singularities are the poles and cuts determined by the rule of Sec. 6-4. This means in particular that there are no singularities at points where s, t, and u are all complex, i.e., no complex singularities. This hypothesis has been verified to be true for the first few orders of perturbation theory.

We can thus get the picture of all singularities of A(s,t,u) for proton-neutron scattering by just picking up the poles and cuts shown in Figs. 6-3, 6-5, and 6-6. This is shown in Fig. 6-7. For simplicity, we have just indicated the poles and the first cuts in s, t, and u, respectively.

6-7 APPLICATION TO THE PROPERTIES OF NUCLEON-NUCLEON POTENTIAL

Mandelstam's hypothesis gives the position of the singularities in t and u. We know that in nonrelativistic theory these singularities are determined by the potentials. Conversely, we shall now consider that the characteristics of the potential are in fact determined by the t and u singularities which are related to the possible intermediate

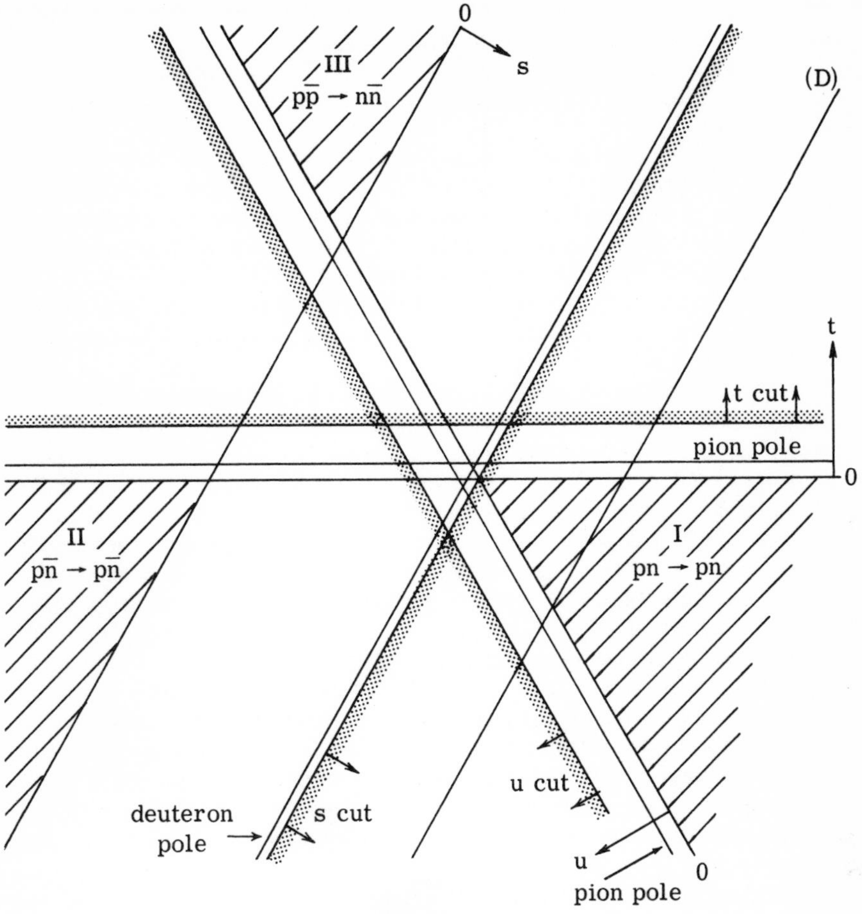

Figure 6-7

states in the crossed reactions. It will be interesting to see now what Mandelstam's hypothesis predicts for the nucleon-nucleon potential.

The t singularity which is nearest to the physical region is the pion pole. To see what contribution this pole gives to the direct proton-neutron potential, it would be necessary to know something of its residue.

Perturbation theory gives us the answer, which is very nearly the same as what was found in Chapter 3, Eq. (3-9).

$$A(s,t,u) = \frac{g^2}{t - \mu^2} + \text{regular part}$$

The residue is a constant here, or a Legendre polynomial of zeroth degree, because the spin of the pion is zero.

We can picture this pion pole as in Fig. 6-8 (analogous to Fig. 6-2), where the pion is a virtual intermediate state between the initial and final states.

Let us now go back to proton-neutron potential. The contribution of the pion pole to $A(s,t,u)$ is $g^2/(t - \mu^2)$ but, as we have seen in Chapter 3, this is nothing but the contribution of the Born approximation of a simple Yukawa potential $g^2(e^{-\mu r}/r)$ to the scattering amplitude whose range is the pion Compton wavelength μ^{-1}.

The customary interpretation of that result is that the proton and neutron can exchange a pion as shown in Fig. 6-9, which is the same as Fig. 6-8 except for crossing.

A simple approximate calculation will convince us that the exchange of such a pion will actually generate an interaction whose range is $\overline{\mu}^1$: When a neutron emits a pion, the energy is changed by an amount $\Delta E = \mu$. This $\pi - n$ state is thus unstable, and, as indicated by the fourth Heisenberg uncertainty relation, it can last only a time $\mathfrak{T} = 1/\Delta E = \mu^{-1}$. During that time, the π, if it travels with light velocity $c = 1$, will go to a distance $r = \mathfrak{T} = \mu^{-1}$, where it will be caught by the proton. Therefore the range of $p - n$ interaction will be of the order of μ^{-1}.

The next singularity of $A(s,t,u)$ is the cut at $t = 4\mu^2$. It can lead only to a potential of range $1/2\mu$. Therefore, this two-pion cut will lead to a $1/2\mu$ range for the residual interaction. The two-pion cut contribution to the interaction is customarily thought of as being due to the exchange of two pions between the nucleons, as shown in Fig. 6-10. Then, in the same way, the three-pion cut will correspond to three-pion exchange, and so on.

6-8 EXCHANGE OF OTHER PARTICLES

To calculate the relation between the properties of the cuts and the potential is outside the scope of these notes. However, it is worthwhile to see how a momentum-transfer cut may contribute to the physphysical values of the scattering amplitude.

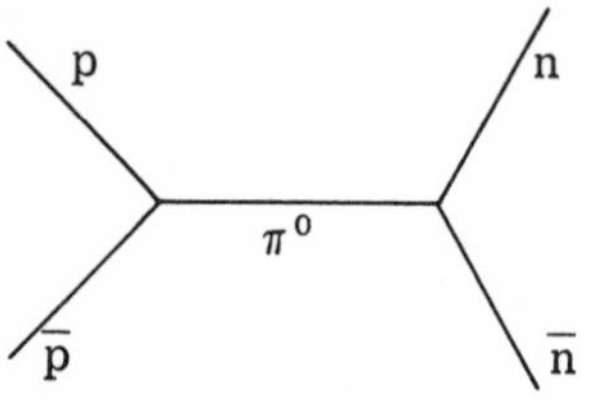

Figure 6-8

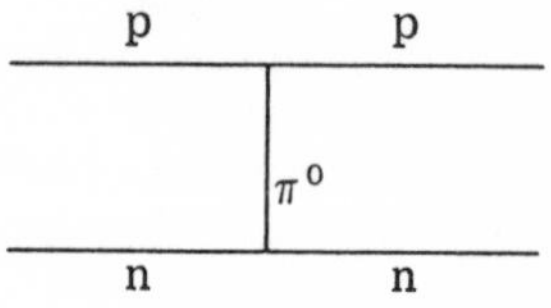

Figure 6-9

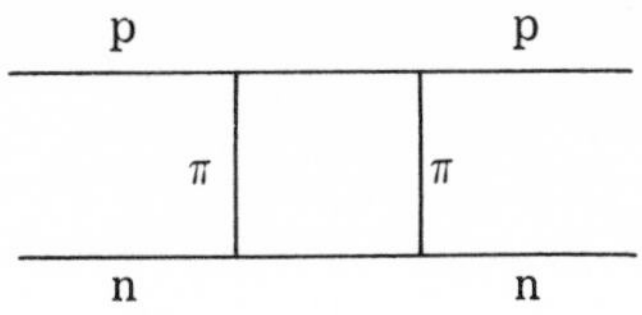

Figure 6-10

For the nonrelativistic case, it was shown in Chapter 3 that, if we have a scattering amplitude $f(p^2, \cos\theta)$ defined for complex values of p^2, then the physical amplitude will be the limit of that function for a p tending to $p + i\varepsilon$. That must still be correct for the nonrelativistic region of A(s,t,u) and is in fact even true for all values of s. The scattering amplitude will thus be given by taking (s,t,u) in the physical region I, s having an infinitesimal imaginary part. Consider then the function of t,$A(s + i\varepsilon, t)$ where s is kept fixed and larger than $4m^2$ (it is necessary to indicate the sign of the small imaginary part of s because of the energy cut $s > 4m^2$). The singularities of A(s,t,u) are now the pole at $t = \mu^2$ and the cut starting from $t = 4\mu^2$, the pole at $u = \mu^2$, i.e., $4m^2 - s - t = \mu^2$ or $t = 4m^2 - \mu^2 - s$ and the cut starting from $u = 4\mu^2$. The simplest way to determine these singularities consists in fixing s on the straight line (D) of Fig. 6-7 and reading up the singularities on the two-dimensional plot. We shall thus get the singularities as indicated on Fig. 6-11.

The value of A(s,t,u) in the physical region, i.e., for $0 > t > 4m^2 - s$ will then be given by a Cauchy formula

$$A(s,t) = \frac{1}{2\pi i}\int_C \frac{A(s,t')\,dt'}{t' - t} \tag{6-6}$$

where t is the contour shown in Fig. 6-12.

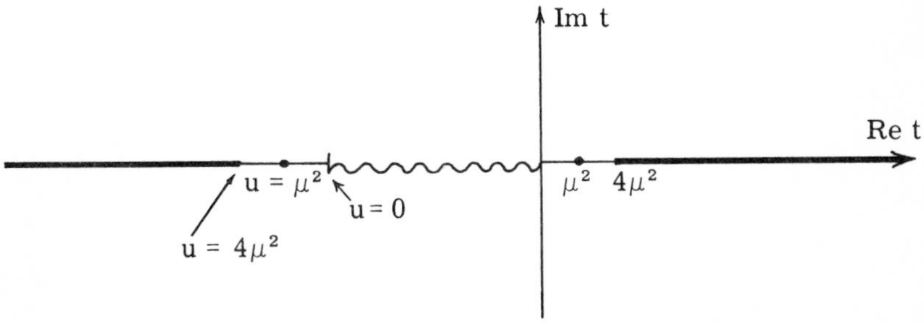

Figure 6-11

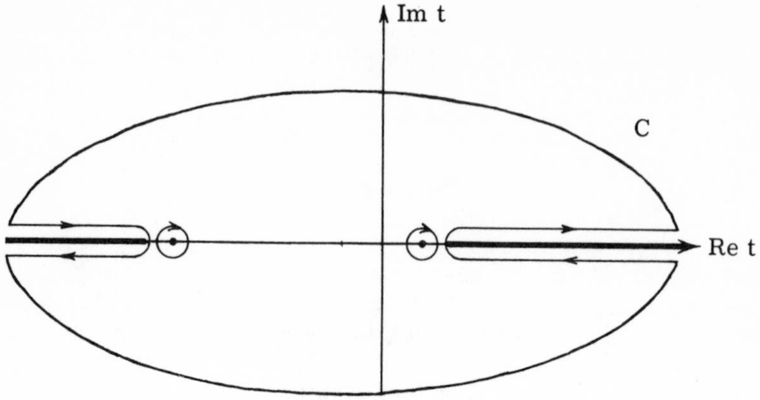

Figure 6-12

Let us suppose that A(s,t,u) tends sufficiently rapidly to zero when t tends to infinity, so that the contribution of the large circle to (6-6) may be neglected. The contribution of the pole $t = \mu^2$ is simply $g^2/(t - \mu^2)$ since g^2 is the residue of that pole. The contribution of the pole $u = \mu^2$ will also be $g^2/(u - \mu^2)$. The contribution from the right-hand cut is

$$\frac{1}{2\pi i} \int_{4\mu^2}^{\infty} \frac{A(s, t' + i\varepsilon) - A(s, t' - i\varepsilon)}{t' - t}\, dt'$$

i.e., defining the function $A_t(s,t)$ on the t cut:

$$\frac{1}{2i}[A(s, t' + i\varepsilon) - A(s, t' - i\varepsilon)] = A_t(s,t) \qquad (6\text{-}7)$$

This t cut will contribute to A(s,t) by

$$\frac{1}{\pi} \int_{4\mu^2}^{\infty} \frac{A_t(s,t')\, dt'}{t' - t}$$

The left-hand cut may be treated in the same way, just replacing t by u, so that

$$A(s,t,u) = \frac{g^2}{t - \mu^2} + \frac{g^2}{u - \mu^2} + \frac{1}{\pi}\int_{4\mu^2}^{\infty} \frac{A_t(s,t')\, dt'}{t' - t} + \frac{1}{\pi}\int_{4\mu^2}^{\infty} \frac{A_u(s,u')\, du}{u' - u} \qquad (6\text{-}8)$$

Here we find again the contributions to the amplitude from the poles, analogous to the first Born approximation of a Yukawa potential. The important new point is that we see that the contributions from the cuts are proportional to the *discontinuities* A_t, A_u and will be largest for the smallest values of t′, u′.

It is possible to give explicit expressions for the discontinuity A_t in terms of A(s,t,u) and of the pion-pion scattering amplitude. However, we shall not enter into these developments, which are given in the book by G. F. Chew (see the Bibliography).

An interesting application of (6-8) is that we can see how the exchange of an unstable particle like the ρ meson will contribute to the the nucleon-nucleon amplitude. Let us recall that the ρ meson is in fact a two-pion resonance of mass 5.5 μ. If it were a stable particle, it could then be exchanged by the nucleons just like the π meson (Fig. 6-13), giving a pole to A(s,t,u) and a contribution

$$\frac{g^2\, NN\rho}{t - m_\rho^2} \qquad (6\text{-}9)$$

However, as it is a resonance, its mass is not well defined and the mass distribution of the ρ, i.e., the probability of finding a given mass for the 2π into which the ρ can disintegrate, is a function $\sigma(m^2)$, where $\sigma(m^2)$ is a Breit-Wigner function, as shown in Fig. 6-14, so that (6-9) would rather take the form

$$\int \sigma(m^2)\, \frac{g_{NN\rho}(m^2)}{t - m^2}\, dm^2 \qquad (6\text{-}10)$$

It may be shown that the discontinuity $A_t(s,t')$ which describes the

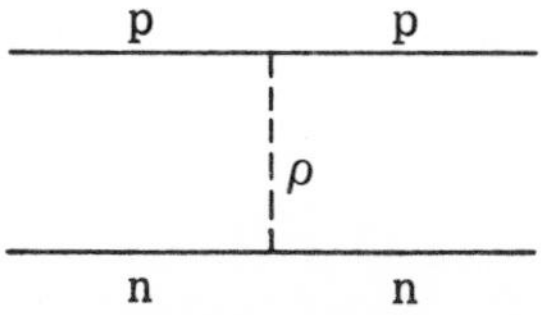

Figure 6-13

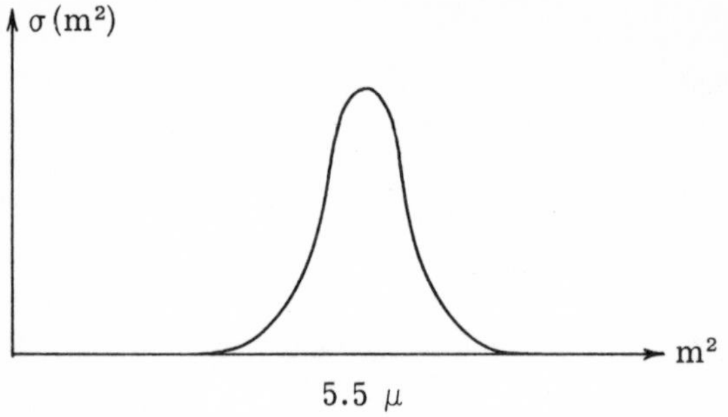

Figure 6-14

contribution of two-meson exchange to A(s,t,u) has in fact a form very close to that of $\sigma(m^2)$, i.e., that Mandelstam's representation provides a way to take into account the mutual interaction of exchanged particles, as shown in Fig. 6-15. It is indeed clear that, if $A_t(s,t') = \sigma(t')g^2_{NN\rho}(t')$, (6-10) is identical to part of (6-8). This is one of the important advantages of Mandelstam's representation over perturbation field-theoretic calculations.

6-9 APPLICATION TO PION-NUCLEON SCATTERING

We have indicated in Fig. 6-16 the singularities which appear in pion-nucleon scattering. This is a complement to Fig. 5-10. These singularities are:

In the s variable

A pole corresponding to the nucleon as an intermediate one-particle state between the initial and final pion-nucleon states (Fig. 6-17). The same argument as for the pion pole in nucleon-nucleon scattering shows that the residue is equal to the square of the pion-nucleon coupling constant g^2.

An elastic cut starting at $s = (m + \mu)^2$ and further inelastic cuts, the first one starting at $(m + 2\mu)^2$ and corresponding respectively to the opening of the $\pi - N$ and $2\pi - N$ channels.

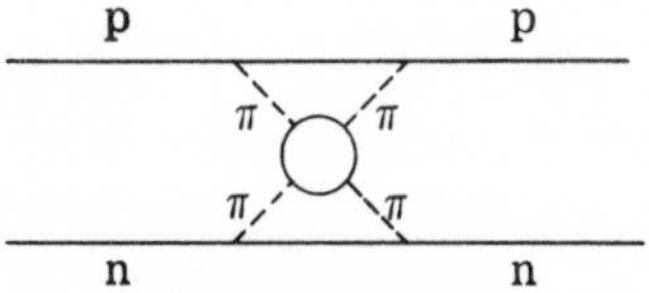

Figure 6-15

In the u variable

As the crossed reaction is identical with the direct one, the singularities on s and u are the same.

In the t variable

The crossed reaction is $N\overline{N} \to \pi\pi$.

There is no one-particle intermediate state. In fact, the only such possible particle would be a pion. However the coupling (Fig. 6-18) is

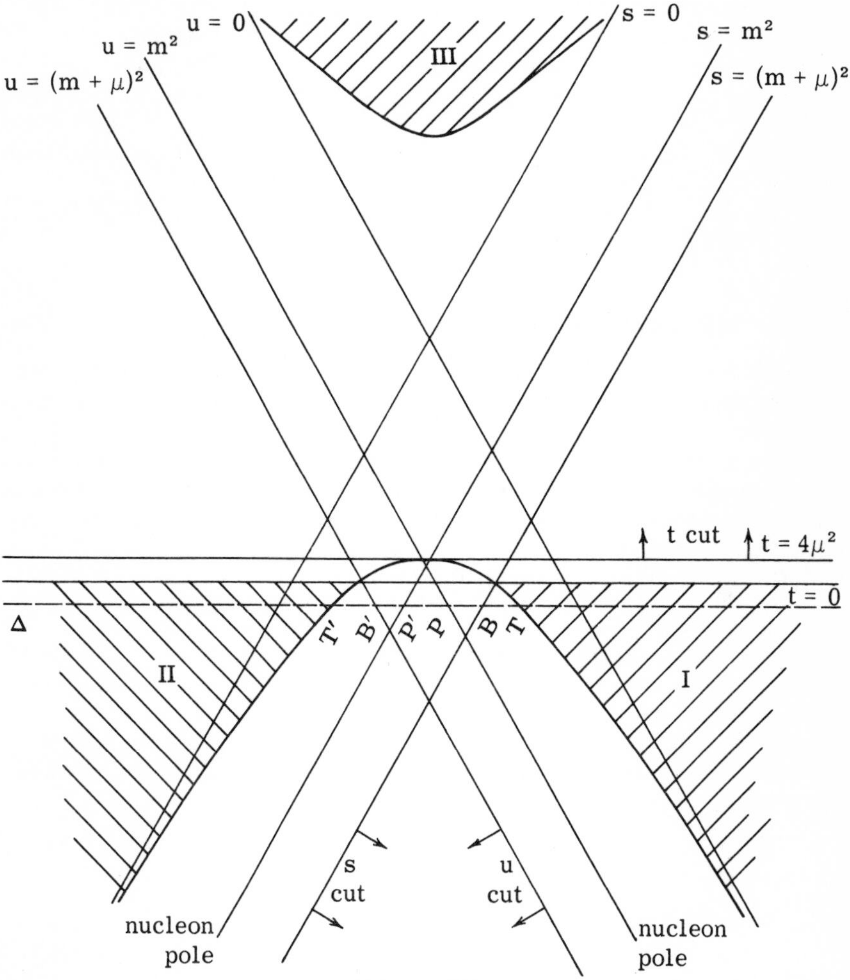

Figure 6-16

(We have grossly exaggerated the mass μ of the pion with respect to the mass m of the nucleon.)

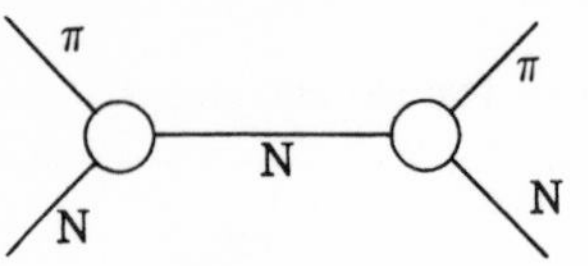

Figure 6-17

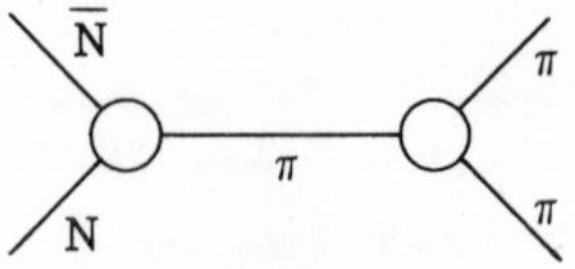

Figure 6-18

impossible. In fact, as the intermediate pion has spin zero, the two final pions would have the same angular momenta. Then their total parity is positive and is opposite to that of the intermediate pion. Therefore there is no one-particle pole.

There is a cut at $t = (2\mu)^2$ corresponding to the opening of the two-pion reaction channel. Then there are other cuts at $(4\mu)^2$, and so on. (It may be shown that, owing to isotopic spin conservation, there cannot be a three-pion cut.)

This plot will be used in Sec. 6-12 to discuss pion-nucleon dispersion relations.

6-10 THE HIGH-ENERGY DOMAIN

Relativistic features of the interactions will certainly show themselves most clearly in high-energy experiments, which we shall now consider more closely.

One of the most crucial facts at high energy is the number of many-particle channels which open as the energy increases. We thus have to deal first with the inelastic reactions and their influence on elastic scattering.

We write, as in Chapter 2, Eq. (2-11),

$$A(s,t) = \sum_{\ell=0}^{\infty} (2\ell + 1) a_\ell(s) P_\ell(\cos\theta) \tag{6-11}$$

where θ is the scattering angle in the s channel. We have seen in Chapter 2 that the ratio between the outgoing and the incoming waves was $e^{2i\delta_\ell} = 1 + 2ika_\ell$.

Now, we have changed slightly the definition of a_ℓ, by introducing a factor of $\sqrt{s}$ in the passage from f to A (6-5). The ratio is now $e^{2i\delta_\ell} = 1 + (2ik/\sqrt{s})\,a_\ell(s)$.

If there is some inelasticity, we must have a ratio less than one in modulus:

$$\left| 1 + \frac{2ik}{\sqrt{s}} a_\ell(s) \right| < 1 \tag{6-12}$$

The elastic cross section is still given by (1-4), or:

$$\frac{d\sigma_{el}}{d\Omega} = \frac{1}{s} |A(s,t)|^2 \tag{6-13}$$

By integration over all angles, using the orthogonality of Legendre polynomials, we find the total elastic cross section:

$$\sigma_{el} = \frac{4\pi}{s} \sum_{\ell=0}^{\infty} (2\ell + 1) |a_\ell|^2 \tag{6-14}$$

The inelastic cross section will be clearly proportional to what has been removed from the incoming wave, that is, to

$$1 - \left| 1 + \frac{2ik}{\sqrt{s}} a_\ell(s) \right|^2$$

The normalization factor is more delicate to find, but we refer the reader to any textbook on the matter and get

$$\sigma_{inel} = \pi \sum_{\ell=0}^{\infty} (2\ell + 1) \frac{1 - \left| 1 + \frac{2ik}{\sqrt{s}} a_\ell \right|^2}{k^2} \tag{6-15}$$

The total cross section is then

$$\sigma_t = \sigma_{el} + \sigma_{inel}$$

i.e., after a simple calculation

$$\sigma_t = \pi \sum_{\ell=0}^{\infty} (2\ell + 1) \frac{4 \operatorname{Im} a_\ell}{k\sqrt{s}} \tag{6-16}$$

There is a remarkable relation between the total cross section and the scattering amplitude. In fact, let us consider the forward scattering amplitude which is obtained by letting θ vanish. As $P_\ell(1) = 1$ one has trivially

$$A(s,0) = \sum (2\ell + 1) a_\ell \tag{6-17}$$

Comparing (6-16) and (6-17) we get immediately the so-called "optical theorem," which relates the total cross section and the imaginary part of the forward scattering amplitude. It is well known in nonrelativistic quantum mechanics, where it reads

$$\mathrm{Im}\{f(k^2, \cos\theta = 1)\} = \frac{k\sigma_t}{4\pi} \qquad \text{(Bohr-Peierls-Placzek relation)} \tag{6-18}$$

With our invariant amplitude, it reads

$$\mathrm{Im}\, A(s,t)\Big|_{t=0} = \frac{k\sqrt{s}\;\sigma_t}{4\pi} \tag{6-19}$$

For most elementary-particle-proton scatterings, such as proton-proton, proton-antiproton, pion-proton, $K^{\pm}$ meson-proton, one has fairly good measurements of the total cross section σ_t and the differential elastic cross section. A comparison between these two quantities makes it possible to determine both the imaginary part and the real part of $f(s,0)$. The imaginary part is actually given by the total cross section through the optical theorem (6-19), while the real part may be derived from the knowledge of $\mathrm{Im}\, f(s,0)$ and of the forward elastic cross section through (1-11), i.e.,

$$\frac{d\sigma}{d\Omega}\Big|_{\theta=0} = \frac{1}{s}\,[(\mathrm{Re}\, A(s,0))^2 + (\mathrm{Im}\, A(s,0))^2]$$

The experimental results show that, while $\mathrm{Im}\, A(s,0)$ increases with energy, the ratio $\mathrm{Re}\, A(s,0)/\mathrm{Im}\, A(s,0)$ decreases until ultimately it cannot be distinguished from zero within the experimental errors. Consequently, one has, from (6-11),

$$\frac{\mathrm{Re}\, A(s,0)}{\mathrm{Im}\, A(s,0)} = \left[\sum (2\ell + 1)\, \mathrm{Re}\, a_\ell(s)\right] \frac{4\pi\sqrt{s}}{k\sigma_t} \to 0 \tag{6-20}$$

This relation suggests strongly that the real part of each $a_\ell(s)$ tends to zero as compared with the imaginary parts, i.e., that $A(s,t)$ may in fact be considered as purely imaginary.

This property of the amplitude may be understood in terms of the so-called optical model, which we shall consider in a definite example, that of pion-nucleon scattering. Let us suppose that the nucleon has a finite extension R and that a pion hits it with its momentum p directed in the z direction (Fig. 6-19). When p is very large, one can allow uncertainties Δp_x and Δp_y of the components of p perpendicular to z small with respect to p without affecting the definition of the incoming momentum, i.e., one can define the coordinates x and y with such uncertainties that

$$\Delta x \ll R \qquad \Delta y \ll R$$

as long as $p \gg R^{-1}$. (We recall that $\hbar = 1$ in our units.) In fact, this

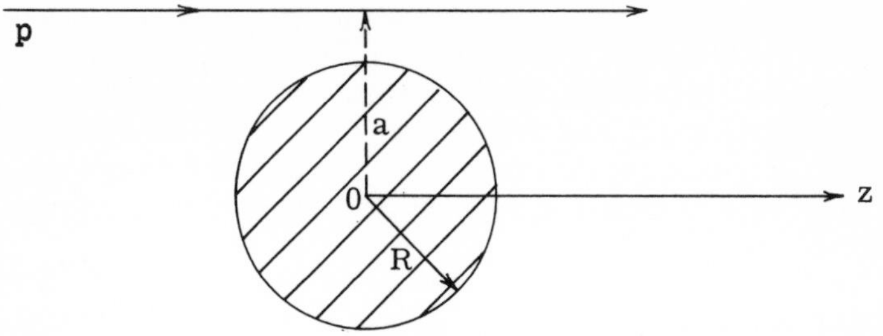

Figure 6-19

means that the wavelength is small with respect to R. The distance $b = \sqrt{x^2 + y^2}$ from the nucleon center to the pion line of flight is called the impact parameter, and we see that it is fairly well defined when the momentum is large enough.

As the nucleon has the extension R, the pion will not interact when b is larger than R. This may be expressed in terms of partial-wave amplitudes if we remark that the pion angular momentum ℓ is equal to pb. Thus, for $\ell > pR$ there will be no interaction, or

$$a_\ell = 0 \qquad \text{for } \ell > pR \tag{6-21}$$

When the pion actually hits the target, i.e., $b < R$, several possibilities are open. As there will be inelastic collisions at these high energies, the coefficients a_ℓ will satisfy inequality (6-11). An extreme case is attained when $1 + (2ik/\sqrt{s})\, a_\ell$ is zero, for the inelastic cross section (6-15) then attains its maximum value. One says that in that case the nucleon is "black," using the language of optics: it is the definition of a black body that it should absorb all photons which hit it. When, on the contrary, $|1 + (2ik/\sqrt{s})\, a_\ell| = 1$, one says that the nucleon is "transparent." In the intermediate cases, the nucleon is said to be "gray." For a black nucleon one has

$$a_\ell = \frac{i\sqrt{s}}{2k} \qquad \text{for } \ell < pR \tag{6-22}$$

i.e., a_ℓ is purely imaginary as is the total scattering amplitude A(s,t).

Collecting the expressions (6-21) and (6-22) for a_ℓ and inserting them into the formulas (6-15) and (6-16) for σ_{inel} and σ_t, we get

$$\sigma_{inel} = \pi R^2$$

$$\sigma_t = 2\pi R^2$$

Note that the total cross section is twice the inelastic, i.e., that the elastic and inelastic cross sections are equal. This result is in fact well known from optics: when a black sphere, whose radius is much larger than the wavelength, absorbs light, it scatters by diffraction as much light as it has absorbed (this is a consequence of Babinet's principle). For this reason, high-energy scattering where the scattering amplitude is purely imaginary is often called diffraction scattering.

A characteristic feature of such a scattering is that all the elastic scattering is confined inside a small angle $\theta \simeq (pR)^{-1}$, so that a typical high-energy differential cross section has the aspect of Fig. 6-20. It shows a peaking in the forward direction which is called the "diffraction peak."

6-11 ASYMPTOTIC PROPERTIES OF A(s,t,u)

One may wonder what limitations are imposed by the Mandelstam hypothesis on the behavior of the amplitude A(s,t,u) at high energies. To be definite, we shall again consider pion-nucleon scattering.

The Mandelstam hypothesis fixes essentially the position of the momentum transfer cuts (at $t = 4\mu^2$ in the case of $\pi - N$ scattering), i.e., it tells us that, at a given fixed energy, the scattering is the same as would be produced by a superposition of Yukawa potentials whose ranges are smaller than $(2\mu)^{-1}$. The potential which could be determined by that condition would generally be complex and would depend upon energy, but its essential property of a finite range will remain, even at very high energy.

In place of the whole superposition of Yukawa potentials, let us for simplicity consider a single potential $V = g(e^{-Kr}/r)$, where g is a complex function of s while K, which may itself vary with energy, is bounded from below by $K^2 > 4\mu^2$.

At high energy the impact parameter b may be considered as

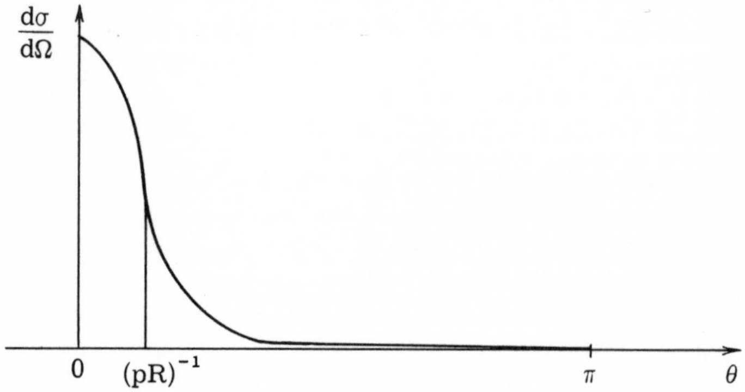

Figure 6-20

meaningful. Calling p the pion momentum and E its energy, one may neglect the pion mass and write $p = E - V$, As V is complex, the wave function e^{ipx} will show absorption, the total absorption being defined quantitatively by the total potential "seen" by the pion, i.e.,

$$U(b) = \int_{-\infty}^{+\infty} V(r)\, dz \qquad \text{with } z^2 + b^2 = r^2$$

If $|U(b)| \ll 1$, the pion will not interact while if $|U(b)|$ is much larger than 1, the pion will certainly interact. Now U(b) will be of the order ge^{-Kb}, and it will be equal to 1 for $b = R$ such that

$$|g|\, e^{-KR} = 1 \qquad \text{i.e., } R = \frac{1}{K} \log|g|$$

and the total cross section will be of the order πR^2.

To determine the possible values of the total cross section it is necessary to know something about the possible behavior of g, i.e., of the discontinuity[†] of the scattering amplitude on the momentum-transfer cuts when s is large. It is commonly assumed that the total amplitude A(s,t,u) together with all its discontinuities cannot increase for large values of s more rapidly than a fixed power of s: s^u. This hypothesis is necessary, as we shall see in Sec. 6-12, in order to be able to write dispersion relations. Therefore, $\log|g|$ is at most of the order of n log s and the total cross section will be at most of the order

$$\sigma \simeq \text{constant} \times \log^2 s \tag{6-23}$$

i.e., the Mandelstam hypothesis puts a strong limitation on the possible asymptotic behavior of cross sections. They cannot increase more rapidly than the squared logarithm of the energy.

If we use the optical theorem in the form (6-19) and suppose that Re A(s,0) is always smaller than Im A(s,0), the preceding result shows that the forward amplitude A(s,0) cannot increase more rapidly than

$$A(s,0) \sim \text{constant} \times s \log^2 s \tag{6-24}$$

This proof has been put into a rigorous form, with the same hypotheses.

Actually, the condition (6-24) leads to severe consistency requirements for the theory. Suppose, for instance, that there exists a bound state with angular momentum ℓ larger than 1, say, $\ell = 2$, in the

---

† g is somehow an average of A_t [cf. (6-8)].

t channel. Let us suppose that all scattering particles have equal masses μ. Call M the mass of this bound state. The bound state will lead to a pole:

$$A(s,t) = G^2 \frac{P_2(\cos\theta_t)}{t - M^2} + \text{regular} \qquad \cos\theta_t = 1 + \frac{2s}{t - 4\mu^2}$$

or, as $P_2(x) = \frac{1}{2}(3x^2 - 1)$, for large enough values of s, the pole term will be

$$6G^2 \frac{s^2}{(t - M^2)(t - 4\mu^2)^2} \tag{6-25}$$

A(s,t) increases like s^2 when t is close enough to M, as no cancellation can take place: the pole term dominates.

It is a fundamental question to reconcile the asymptotic behavior (6-24) of A(s,t,u) on the boundary of the physical region and the much stronger asymptotic behavior of the pole terms (6-25). It is in fact necessary that some cancellation occur between the pole terms and the contribution to A(s,t) of the t cut in order to lead to the behavior (6-24). The Regge pole hypothesis automatically provides that cancellation, as we shall see in Chapter 7, and this is one of its most attractive features from the theoretical standpoint.

6-12 DISPERSION RELATIONS

As an illustration of the use of complex-variables techniques, we shall now derive dispersion relations for pion-nucleon scattering (neglecting the nucleon spin).

The Mandelstam hypothesis gives us the analytic properties of the amplitude A(s,t,u) as a function of the complex variables s, t, and u. If we fix t at a real negative value, the amplitude will be only a function of the complex variable s, or, equivalently, of $u = 2m^2 + 2\mu^2 - t - s$. The singularities of that function are immediately read in Fig. 6-16 and they are (see dashed line Δ in Fig. 6-16):

1. A cut starting from the point B at $s = (m + \mu)^2$ and running to $+\infty$ (it is in fact, as we have seen, a superposition of several cuts but that will not matter here).
2. The nucleon pole P at $s = m^2$ with residue g^2.
3. Another nucleon pole P′ at $u = m^2$.
4. Another cut from B at $u = (m + \mu)^2$ to $u = +\infty$.

Part of the real s axis is within the two physical regions I and II starting from a threshold T to $s = +\infty$ and from a threshold T′ to $u = +\infty$. T (resp. T′) is on the right (resp. the left) of B (resp. B′) except for $t = 0$, where the two points coincide. All these results are shown in Fig. 6-21.

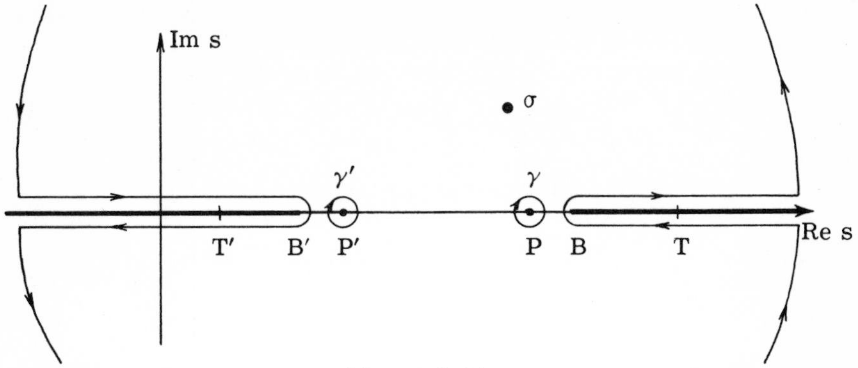

Figure 6-21

The value of A(s,t) for a complex value σ of s may be written by a Cauchy formula.

$$A(\sigma,t) = \frac{1}{2\pi i} \int_C \frac{A(s',t)\, ds'}{s' - \sigma} \tag{6-26}$$

where the contour C encloses all singularities and is shut by two large semicircles in the upper and the lower part of the complex s plane.

Generally, the integration on these two semicircles will give contributions to (6-26), except if A(s′,t) tends to zero when the modulus of s′ tends to infinity. Let us first suppose that such is the case.

The contribution to (6-26) of the small circle γ enclosing P will clearly be

$$-\frac{1}{2\pi i} \oint_\gamma \frac{g^2}{s' - m^2} \frac{ds'}{s' - \sigma}$$

where the integration on γ is made in the counterclockwise sense. That will give, again by Cauchy's formula,

$$\frac{g^2}{\sigma - m^2} \tag{6-27}$$

The integration along γ' will give

$$-\frac{1}{2\pi i} \oint_{\gamma'} \frac{g^2}{u' - m^2} \frac{ds'}{s' - \sigma}$$

(counterclockwise)

where we can replace $s' - \sigma$ by $-(u' - U)$ and ds' by $-du'$ so that we shall get

$$\frac{g^2}{U - m^2} \qquad \text{where } U = 2m^2 + 2\mu^2 - \sigma - t \tag{6-28}$$

The integral on the contour enclosing the right-hand cut will give

$$\frac{1}{2\pi i} \int_{(m+\mu)^2}^{\infty} \frac{[A(s' + i\varepsilon, t) - A(s' - i\varepsilon, t)]\, ds'}{s' - \sigma} \tag{6-29}$$

The amplitude $A(s,t)$ is real for t real and negative, $(m - \mu)^2 - t < s < (m + \mu)^2$. (This has been seen in Chapter 3 for the nonrelativistic amplitude and will remain true in the relativistic case.) Thus

$$\frac{1}{2i} [A(s' + i\varepsilon, t) - A(s' - i\varepsilon, t)] = \operatorname{Im} A(s',t)$$

where, in the right-hand side, we have written the physical amplitude. The expression (6-29) takes the form

$$\frac{1}{\pi} \int_{(m+\mu)^2}^{\infty} \frac{\operatorname{Im} A(s',t)\, ds'}{s' - \sigma} \tag{6-30}$$

In the same way, the contour enclosing the left-hand cut would give

$$-\frac{1}{\pi} \int_{-\infty}^{B'} \frac{\operatorname{Im} A(u',t)\, ds'}{s' - \sigma} = \frac{1}{\pi} \int_{(m+\mu)^2}^{\infty} \frac{\operatorname{Im} A(u',t)\, du'}{u' - U} \tag{6-31}$$

Collecting (6-27), (6-28), (6-30), and (6-31) we get

$$A(\sigma,t) = \frac{g^2}{\sigma - m^2} + \frac{g^2}{U - m^2} + \frac{1}{\pi} \int_{(m+\mu)^2}^{\infty} \frac{\operatorname{Im} A(s',t)\, ds'}{s' - \sigma}$$

$$+ \frac{1}{\pi} \int_{(m+\mu)^2}^{\infty} \frac{\operatorname{Im} A(u',t)\, du'}{u' - U} \tag{6-32}$$

Equation (6-32) will become an equation for the physical amplitude if we let σ tend to $s + i\varepsilon$, where s is a real value on the right of T. When this limit is made, one has to be cautious about the first integral, for one has then

$$\frac{1}{\pi} \int_{(m+\mu)^2}^{\infty} \frac{\operatorname{Im} A(s',t)\, ds'}{s' - s - i\varepsilon} \tag{6-33}$$

It may be shown that the integral (6-33) goes to a finite limit as $\varepsilon \to 0$, if the integrand has suitable continuity properties. Actually, we need only take the real part of both sides of (6-32),

$$\operatorname{Re} \frac{1}{\pi} \int_{(m+\mu)^2}^{\infty} \frac{\operatorname{Im} A(s',t)\, ds'}{s' - s - i\varepsilon}$$

$$= \frac{1}{\pi} \int_{(m+\mu)^2}^{\infty} \operatorname{Im} A(s',t) \frac{s' - s}{(s' - s)^2 + \varepsilon^2}\, ds' \tag{6-34}$$

All other terms are real. The limit as $\varepsilon \to 0$ of the integral (6-34) is denoted by

$$\lim_{\varepsilon \to 0} \frac{1}{\pi} \int_{(m+\mu)^2}^{\infty} \operatorname{Im} A(s',t) \frac{s' - s}{(s' - s)^2 + \varepsilon^2}\, ds'$$

$$\equiv \frac{1}{\pi} \mathcal{P} \int_{(m+\mu)^2}^{\infty} \operatorname{Im} A(s',t) \frac{ds'}{s' - s} \tag{6-35}$$

(read $\mathcal{P}$ as "principal part of"). It exists under very weak continuity conditions, for example $|\operatorname{Im} A(s,t) - \operatorname{Im} A(s',t)| \leq C|s - s'|^{\alpha}$ $(\alpha > 0)$. We have thus obtained the following integral relation:

$$\operatorname{Re} A(s,t) = \frac{g^2}{s - m^2} + \frac{g^2}{u - m^2} + \frac{1}{\pi} \mathcal{P} \int_{(m+\mu)^2}^{\infty} \frac{\operatorname{Im} A(s',t)\, ds'}{s' - s}$$

$$+ \frac{1}{\pi} \int_{(m+\mu)^2}^{\infty} \frac{\operatorname{Im} A(u',t)\, du'}{u' - u} \tag{6-36}$$

which is known as a *dispersion relation.*

The dispersion relation (6-36) has a particularly interesting form for zero momentum transfer t. Consider, for instance, the case of π^--proton scattering. Then, as shown by the optical theorem, relation (6-19), Im A(s,0) may be simply expressed as $k\sqrt{s}\,\sigma_t^{(-)}(s)/4\pi$, where $\sigma_t^{(-)}$ is the total p-π^- cross section. In the same way, Im A(u′,t) is the imaginary part of the forward scattering amplitude for the crossed reaction, which is π^+-p scattering, so that it is equal to $q\sqrt{u}\,\sigma_t^{(+)}(u)/4\pi$, where $\sigma_t^{(+)}$ is the total π^+-p cross section and q is the π^+-p c.m. momentum.

The left-hand member may be deduced from a measurement of the forward scattering amplitude

$$\left.\frac{d\sigma^{el}}{d\Omega}\right|_{\theta=0} = \frac{1}{s}(\mathrm{Re}\,A(s,0))^2 + \frac{1}{s}(\mathrm{Im}\,A(s,0))^2$$

so that (6-36) relates only measurable quantities:

$$\mathrm{Re}\,A(s,0) = \frac{g^2}{s-m^2} + \frac{g^2}{u-m^2} + \frac{1}{\pi}\,\mathcal{P}\int_{(m+\mu)^2}^{\infty} \frac{k'\sqrt{s'}\,\sigma_t^-(s')\,ds'}{s'-s} + \frac{1}{\pi}\int_{(m+\mu)^2}^{\infty} \frac{q'\sqrt{u'}\,\sigma_t^+(u')\,du'}{u'-u} \tag{6-37}$$

The measured values of $\sigma_t^{(\pm)}$, however, seem to imply that these cross sections tend to constants when energy becomes very large, so that the integrals do not converge. It is easy to dispose of that difficulty by writing a Cauchy formula for $A(s,0)/(s - s_0)$ in place of writing it for $A(s,0)$. The result of such a formula may be in fact easily guessed from (6-37). Suppose that the integrals in (6-37) converge and subtract the two expressions of (6-37) for a general value of s and for the fixed value s_0, thus getting

$$\begin{aligned}\mathrm{Re}\,A(s,0) - \mathrm{Re}\,A(s_0,0) &= \frac{g^2(s_0-s)}{(s-m^2)(s_0-m^2)} + \frac{g^2(u_0-u)}{(u-m^2)(u_0-m^2)} \\ &+ \frac{s-s_0}{\pi}\,\mathcal{P}\int_{(m+\mu)^2}^{\infty} \frac{k'\sqrt{s'}\,\sigma_t^-(s')\,ds'}{(s'-s)(s'-s_0)} \\ &+ \frac{s_0-s}{\pi}\int_{(m+\mu)^2}^{\infty} \frac{g'\sqrt{u'}\,\sigma_t^+(u')\,du'}{(u'-u)(u'-u_0)}\end{aligned} \tag{6-38}$$

The integrals in this equation are more likely to converge than those in (6-37). This procedure is known as the subtraction method.

The dispersion relation (6-38) corrected for the spin of the proton has been compared with experiment and the agreement is quite good.

The general dispersion relation (6-36) is more difficult to use for a value of t different from zero. In that case, $\mathrm{Im}\,A(s',t)$ must be measured by a determination of the scattering amplitude and this direct measurement is only possible in the physical region. As the integration goes from B to infinity while the physical region goes from T to infinity, there remains an *unphysical region* BT, where Im A(s′,t) is not directly known. Extrapolation procedures, using the Legendre polynomial expansion of A(s,t) out of the physical region, have been devised to express Im A(s′,t) in terms of the phase shifts $\delta_\ell(s')$, but they are subject to rather large experimental uncertainties.

Let us note finally that the dispersion relations for pion-nucleon scattering, for values of t near zero, have been nearly proved from axiomatic field theory using the so-called causality principle, which states that no signal can propagate faster than light. In that respect, the dispersion relations are on a more firm theoretical basis than the Mandelstam theory, which is still only a hypothesis. They are also the most direct test of the physical usefulness of analytic-function techniques.

7

RELATIVISTIC REGGE POLES

7-1 THE PARADOXES

We have seen in Chapter 6 an important point about the apparent conflict between different asymptotic behaviors of the relativistic amplitude. We summarize our findings in the following way: The asymptotic behavior of the amplitude in the forward direction $t = 0$ in the channel where s is the energy squared was shown not to exceed the limiting behavior $s \log^2 s$ (6-23). On the other hand, we saw that if in a crossed channel, say where t is the energy squared, there exists a bound state with a squared mass $t = M^2$, then the asymptotic behavior for t close enough to M^2 is a power of s equal to the angular momentum of the bound state. This is not in itself a contradiction, as we have to deal with two different values of t: 0 and M^2. But it shows that the question of the asymptotic behavior of the amplitude is not as simple as might have been thought, for example, by examination of perturbation-theory terms. In fact, we have to have different asymptotic behaviors of the amplitude as a function of s for different fixed values of t.

Gribov's Paradox

Another, more crucial, paradox was found by Gribov. We can only mention its content here, as the calculations involved are rather complicated. The starting point is the semiclassical diffraction model as described in Chapter 6. One wants to compute the scattering amplitude according to the model of Chapter 6, with a "grayness" which should more or less describe the structure of the colliding particles.

We take it to be independent of energy, just as the total cross section appears to be a constant at high energies. This is the "commonsense" model.

The scattering amplitude turns out then to be very simple at very high energies. It looks like

$$A(s,t) \approx s \cdot g(t) \tag{7-1}$$

where g(t) is easily computed from the absorption coefficient. This of course does not violate the asymptotic condition for $t = 0$.

Let us now for a moment forget about states of high angular momentum, and assume that form (1) holds not only in the diffraction scattering region, that is, for values of t negative (physical), and of the order of $-1/R^2$, where R is the radius of interaction, but also for unphysical values of t, say t positive and of the order of $+1/R^2$. Take, for example, pion-pion scattering (Fig. 7-1). The range of the interaction is such that $1/R^2 \approx 4\mu^2$. So we should have the behavior (7-1) up to values of t corresponding to the t cut.

Now, and this is the part that we have to skip, it has been shown by Gribov that the behavior (7-1) cannot hold on the t cut. Therefore, we find again that the asymptotic behavior in s of the amplitude must change as t varies. If this is so, it surely has very direct connections with the dynamics. Indeed, one of the most clearly dynamical problems is the determination of the binding energy of a bound state. We now know that the energy of a bound state of angular momentum ℓ is that energy where the asymptotic behavior is exactly $(\cos\theta)^{\ell}$.

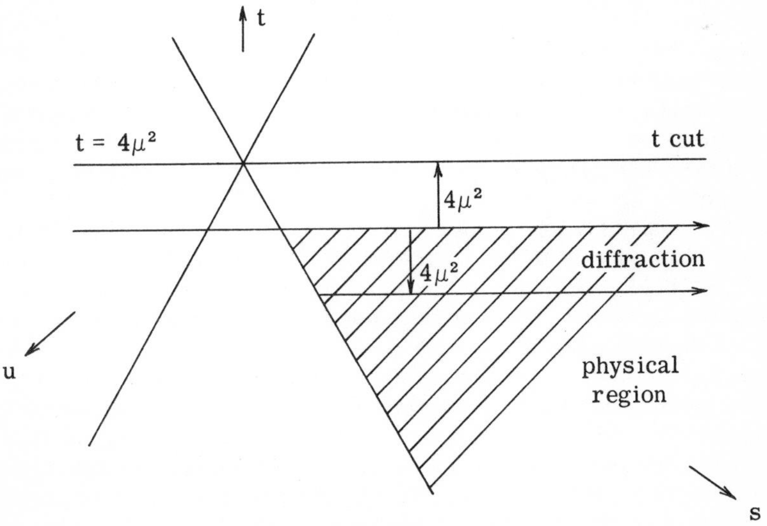

Figure 7-1

Solving the Paradoxes

A way to solve both of these paradoxes together is to abandon a simple-minded asymptotic behavior such as is given by (7-1) and to adopt a variable asymptotic behavior

$$A(s,t) \approx g(t)s^{\alpha(t)} \qquad \text{for } s \to \infty \tag{7-2}$$

where $\alpha(t)$ is some functions of t. It solves the bound-state paradox if we require that $\alpha(t)$ be less than one for $t \leq 0$ (asymptotic condition in the physical region), and $\alpha(M^2)$ be equal to ℓ, angular momentum of a bound state of mass M, in the "t" channel. Of course the pole at $t = M^2$ is contained in the coefficient function g(t). Gribov's paradox also turns out to be solved by this method, if we take $\alpha(t)$ complex when t is on the t cut, which is perfectly reasonable. The diffraction picture which led to behavior (7-1) will have to be altered, in a way which we shall analyze later.

7-2 COMPARISON WITH NONRELATIVISTIC THEORY

The behavior (7-2) was primarily introduced to solve the paradoxes in the simplest way. It showed a very striking likeness to the asymptotic behavior as it exists in potential scattering. We have indeed seen in Chapter 4 that the asymptotic behavior of the nonrelativistic amplitude is given by

$$f(k^2,\theta) \approx \beta(k^2)P_{\alpha(k^2)}(\cos\theta) \approx g(k^2)\Delta^{2\alpha(k^2)}$$

We have only to consider the crossed channel where t is the energy variable, that is, corresponds to k^2, and s is the momentum transfer variable, that is, corresponds to Δ^2, and we find (7-2). This may be a mere coincidence of course, but it was in some way a plausibility argument for the introduction of the behavior (7-2).

In nonrelativistic theory we have seen a way to interpret this asymptotic behavior in terms of an interpolation between partial waves, which displayed the Regge poles, each pole contributing part of the asymptotic behavior. We may now ask the question whether such an interpolation may be done for the relativistic problem and whether it seems to be consistent to assume the existence of Regge poles for it.

The problem of interpolating between partial-wave amplitudes is in itself not well defined. Indeed there are always many interpolating functions. We want however an interpolation which allows one to write a Sommerfeld-Watson formula, that is, with such asymptotic properties in the ℓ plane that one can open up the contour of integration to bring it parallel to the imaginary axis. This condition in fact turns out to be very strong, and, indeed, strong enough to determine uniquely the interpolation (Carlson's theorem). The interpolation was obtained by a trial-and-error method and is defined as follows:

Consider the conventional definition of partial-wave amplitudes [cf. (2-11)],

$$a_\ell(s) = \tfrac{1}{2} \int A(s,t) P_\ell(\cos\theta_s)\, d\cos\theta_s \tag{7-3}$$

$$\cos\theta_s = 1 + \frac{2t}{s-4}$$

(We take for simplicity all masses equal to one.) This does not satisfy our conditions, having a very poor asymptotic behavior:

$$P_\ell(\cos\theta) \approx \operatorname{Sup}\left| e^{i\ell\theta}, e^{-i\ell\theta} \right| \qquad \ell \to \infty \tag{7-4}$$

both ways along the imaginary axis.

The trick which works is now to express $A(s,t)$ by a dispersion relation in t:

$$A(s,t) = \frac{1}{\pi} \int \frac{A_t(s,t')\, dt'}{t'-t} \tag{7-5}$$

We neglect for the moment the pole terms and the u cut. Inserting (7-5) into (7-3) we get

$$a_\ell(s) = \frac{1}{2\pi} \iint \frac{A_t(s,t')\, dt'}{t'-t} P_\ell\left(1 + \frac{2t}{s-4}\right) \frac{2dt}{s-4} \tag{7-6}$$

It is possible to carry out the integration over t for integer ℓ:

$$a_\ell(s) = \frac{1}{\pi} \int A_t(s,t') Q_\ell\left(1 + \frac{2t'}{s-4}\right) \frac{2dt'}{s-4} \tag{7-7}$$

Q_ℓ is the Legendre function of second kind. The passage from (7-6) to (7-7) is possible only for *integer values* of ℓ. For noninteger values it leads to different values for $a_\ell(s)$. We have thus a new kind of interpolation, based now on the Legendre functions of second kind. Let us introduce summarily these newcomers.

$Q_\ell(z)$ is a solution of the usual Legendre equation, where ℓ is taken arbitrary (possibly complex). It behaves at infinity like $\ell!/2^\ell z^{\ell+1}$. It is analytic in z everywhere except for $z = \pm 1$, where it has logarithmic branch points; it is therefore considered as having a cut running along the real axis from $+1$ to $-\infty$. It is analytic in ℓ except when ℓ is a negative integer. At infinity in the ℓ plane it behaves essentially as $\ell^{-1/2}[1/(z + \sqrt{z^2 - 1})^{\ell+1}]$.

This is enough to see that (7-7) defines a very nice interpolation of $a_\ell(s)$, as long as the integral converges. Indeed, for physical s, the quantity $1 + (2t'/s - 4)$ in the Legendre function stays larger than one, and then we have a very nice asymptotic behavior of the integral as a function of ℓ: it decreases exponentially with Re ℓ, and decreases as $1/\ell^{1/2}$ with Im ℓ.

The question of convergence, however, becomes at once crucial, as the behavior of $Q_\ell[1 + (2t'/s - 4)]$ for large t′ is not so nice: it decreases only like $t'^{-\ell-1}$. We have already assumed, in Chapter 6, as everybody does, that the amplitude increases at most like a polynomial at infinity, say like t^n. Then, as

$$A_t(s,t') = \frac{1}{2i}[A(s, t' + i\varepsilon) - A(s, t' - i\varepsilon)]$$

$A_t(s,t')$ increases also, at most like t'^n. This guarantees the convergence of the integral (7-7) as long as Re $\ell > n$, but we do not have any information about what happens for Re $\ell < n$.

This was to be expected. In fact we wanted to have Regge poles for some value of ℓ. The integral (7-7) cannot have any poles as long as it converges, and therefore must diverge as soon as ℓ reaches a Regge pole.

7-3 CHEW'S HYPOTHESIS

We are now in a position to make guesses as to what happens for Re $\ell < n$. There is a very small likelihood that one cannot analytically continue the interpolation $a_\ell(s)$ as defined by (7-7) to the region Re $\ell < n$. Most probably, as often in such problems, there is but one singularity on the line Re $\ell = n$, which is enough for (7-7) to diverge. Then, all bets are open as concerns the location and nature of the other singularities.

One important issue, however, is whether the analytic continuation of $a_\ell(s)$ gives the physical answers for integer $\ell < n$. This is by no means certain, as we have, in deriving (7-7), neglected the subtractions, which would introduce unknown parameters in (7-5) and foul up the connection between (7-3) and (7-7) even for integer $\ell < n$.

Chew has chosen the most economical hypothesis: that the analytic continuation indeed gives the right physical amplitudes for these integer values of $\ell \leq n$. This in principle avoids the introduction of superfluous unknown subtraction constants.

In these conditions, we need to have a well-defined analytic continuation, that is, one which is independent of the way we pass around the singularities. This restricts severely the type of possible singularities: a logarithmic singularity for example would not be convenient.

as the determination of the function is not independent of whether we pass above or below the singularity.

The simplest of all singularities satisfying this uniqueness condition is the pole. We can therefore now state Chew's hypothesis completely:

Postulate: The interpolation defined by (7-7) has an analytic continuation in the region $0 \leq \operatorname{Re} \ell < n$ which leads to the right values of the physical amplitudes for integer ℓ. This analytic continuation has only simple poles, which ensures its one-valuedness.

7-4 EXCHANGE FORCES

While establishing (7-7) we have neglected the u cut, which we recall, is linked with the existence of exchange forces. It is very easy to take it into account, using the same trick as in Chapter 4. We separate the amplitude into two parts, odd and even with respect to $\cos \theta$, and use each to define an interpolation between the odd or even values of ℓ. We simply mention these formulas for the sake of completeness:

$$a_\ell^\pm(s) = \frac{1}{\pi}\int_4^\infty A_t(s,t')Q_\ell\left(1 + \frac{2t'}{s-4}\right)\frac{2dt'}{s-4}$$

$$\pm \frac{1}{\pi}\int_4^\infty A_u(s,u')Q_\ell\left(1 + \frac{2u'}{s-4}\right)\frac{2du'}{s-4} \qquad (7\text{-}8)$$

We have the associated Sommerfeld-Watson formula:

$$A(s,t) = \frac{i}{4}\int \left\{a_\ell^+(s)\left[P_\ell\left(-1 - \frac{2t}{s-4}\right) + P_\ell\left(1 + \frac{2t}{s-4}\right)\right]\right.$$

$$\left. + a_\ell^-\left[P_\ell\left(-1 - \frac{2t}{s-4}\right) - P_\ell\left(1 + \frac{2t}{s-4}\right)\right]\right\}$$

$$\times \frac{(2\ell + 1)\, d\ell}{\sin \Pi\ell} \qquad (7\text{-}9)$$

The contour C is indicated on Fig. 7-2. A typical contribution of the small loop around a pole at $\ell = \alpha$ would be

$$A(s,t) = \frac{\beta(s)}{\sin \Pi\alpha(s)}\left[P_{\alpha(s)}\left(-1 - \frac{2t}{s-4}\right)\right.$$

$$\left. + P_{\alpha(s)}\left(1 + \frac{2t}{s-4}\right)\right] \qquad (7\text{-}10)$$

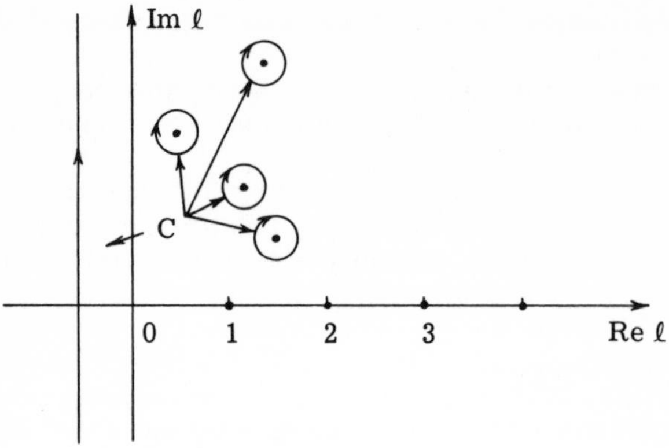

Figure 7-2

if it is a pole of $a_\ell^+(s)$, and

$$A(s,t) = \frac{\beta(s)}{\sin \Pi\alpha(s)} \left[P_{\alpha(s)}\left(-1 - \frac{2t}{s-4}\right) - P_{\alpha(s)}\left(1 + \frac{2t}{s-4}\right)\right] \tag{7-11}$$

if it is a pole of $a_\ell^-(s)$.

We have therefore to distinguish systematically between the poles of $a_\ell^+(s)$ and $a_\ell^-(s)$. We shall say that the first ones have positive *signature*, the second ones negative signature.

7-5 TRAJECTORIES

As we see from (7-10) and (7-11), if the location $\alpha(s)$ of the pole becomes an integer, the sine in the denominator vanishes, and we have a pole of the total amplitude, that is, a bound state, or stable particle, as we have seen now a number of times. This occurs of course only under the condition that the numerator does not vanish simultaneously. But it is clear from (7-10) that the numerator *will* vanish precisely for α integer and odd. Therefore the poles of a_ℓ^+ (signature +) can only contribute bound states with *even* angular momenta, while the poles with signature − can only contribute bound states with odd angular momenta.

Similarly, as we already saw in the case of nonrelativistic scattering, the Regge poles may reach the above integer values for slightly complex values of the energy on the unphysical sheet, thus giving rise to resonances. This corresponds to the case where a Regge pole passes near an integer value for physical, real energy (Fig. 7-3) (cf. Fig. 4-4).

While the energy increases, s follows the solid line, $\alpha(s)$ the corresponding solid line in the ℓ plane. If the energy wanders away in the unphysical sheet (dashed line in the s plane), $\alpha(s)$ makes a similar loop in the ℓ plane, and may thus reach an integer value.

Each Regge pole may therefore, as the energy increases, pass through or near a number of integer values (even or odd according to its signature), and generates thus a whole family of particles, stable or unstable, until the pole goes too far away from the real axis, where it is not possible any more to say anything precise: the concept of unstable particle passes gradually, as the width increases, to that of a resonance, and then fades away when the width becomes so large that neighboring resonances overlap. This will occur when Im $\alpha(s)$ becomes of the order of 2, so that the Regge pole influences several partial waves simultaneously.

7-6 GENERALIZATIONS

In relativistic theory, there are always inelastic processes as soon as the energy is large enough. We have thus to generalize what we have said to the case where several channels are simultaneously present. In this case, we do not have a single amplitude to describe the process, but several, which may depend also on the relative energies of the particles involved, if there are more than two of them.

We can always separate these amplitudes into components of different total angular momentum ℓ, and then guess what happens. For more-than-two-particle states, nobody knows for sure how to interpolate between the partial-wave amplitudes, but let us assume that there is some way to do so, by a function exhibiting analyticity properties in ℓ, analogous to what we have seen for two-particle amplitudes. As the physical interpretation of a Regge pole is in particular

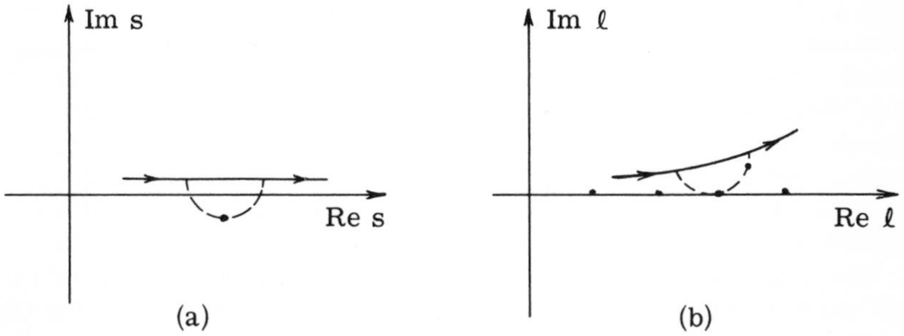

Figure 7-3

a resonance, which can decay in any of the channels open, at the same energy, we shall assume that a given Regge pole appears in all the amplitudes of transition interpolated in ℓ. We have in this way a matrix, whose rows and columns are labeled by the channels, and each element has a pole in ℓ at the same place $\alpha(s)$.

Of course the channels into which a resonance can decay are defined by their quantum numbers, which shows that the Regge poles will be characterized by a set of quantum numbers, and by the signature. All the composite systems having these quantum numbers will undergo the influence of the Regge pole at the suitable angular momenta (even or odd according to the signature), be it in the form of bound state or of resonance.

In the case of the fermions, which we have constantly excluded till now, it is uncertain how one has to take the spin into account. However one would tend to generalize the preceding results by interpolating between values of the *total* angular momentum j. The signature effect will be taken as follows: One kind of Regge pole appears only at values of $j = \frac{1}{2}, \frac{5}{2}, \frac{9}{2}, \ldots$, the other kind at $j = \frac{3}{2}, \frac{7}{2}, \frac{11}{2}, \ldots$.

Factorization Hypothesis

As the Regge poles may be interpreted as resonances, we should expect that they share the properties of resonances. When a resonance can decay into several channels, nuclear-reactions theory teaches us that the cross section for its formation and decay depends upon the product of the partial widths of the formation and decay channels. This factorization of the cross section into a part which depends upon the formation channel and another part which depends upon the decay channel has very interesting consequences, and we should try to see whether it is reasonable in the Regge pole approach.

To see that, we have to keep in mind that, in the case of several channels, which we shall label by Greek indices $\lambda, \mu, \ldots$, the amplitude is in fact a matrix, $a_\ell(s)_{\lambda\mu}$, being the element of the matrix which is the reaction amplitude from channel λ to channel μ. We now have to see what is the most likely form for such a matrix when all elements have a pole in ℓ at $\ell = \alpha$. First, what do we mean by likely? Essentially we mean that we do not have to invoke a coincidence, or else that if we disturb the matrix a little, its structure does not change. Obviously, if we add small perturbations to the elements $a_\ell(s)_{\lambda\mu}$ of the amplitude matrix, we shall not change much at the pole, as all $a_\ell(s)_{\lambda\mu}$ are infinite for $\ell = \alpha$, and are not disturbed by the addition of a small quantity. We do not gain any information here. On the other hand, consider the inverse amplitude matrix $[a_\ell(s)^{-1}]_{\lambda\mu}$. It must have zero eigenvalue, as $a_\ell(s)$ has surely an infinite eigenvalue for $\ell = \alpha$. If I disturb a little the matrix $a_\ell(s)^{-1}$ by adding little quantities to its elements, I shall change the zero eigenvalues a little, which are functions of ℓ, and the different eigenvalues will vanish at different places near α. Now consider the situation: if there is only one zero eigenvalue, the disturbance of the inverse matrix shifts the Regge pole's position a little, and that is all. If there are several zero eigenvalues, the disturbance of the inverse matrix splits the initial Regge pole into several ones, slightly shifted to the locations of the zero eigenvalues of the disturbed inverse matrix. The most likely structure is then that the inverse matrix has only one vanishing eigenvalue, or that $a_\ell(s)$ has only one infinite eigenvalue. Then there is but one eigenvector γ_λ corresponding to this infinite eigenvalue, and $[a_\ell(s)]_{\lambda\mu}$ is proportional to γ_λ for all μ. By time-reversal invariance $[a_\ell(s)]_{\lambda\mu} = [a_\ell(s)]_{\mu\lambda}$ and $[a_\ell(s)]_{\lambda\mu}$ is also proportional to γ_μ for all λ. Thus it follows that

$$[a_\ell(s)]_{\lambda\mu} = \frac{\gamma_\lambda \gamma_\mu}{\ell - \alpha(s)} + \text{finite part} \tag{7-12}$$

The rule is then simple: when there are several channels, each pole contribution (7-10) or (7-11) becomes a matrix, $\beta(s)$ being replaced by a product of the form $\gamma_\lambda \gamma_\mu$. If the matrix is not of this simple form we shall say that we have an accidental coincidence of two or more poles.

8

COMPARISON WITH EXPERIMENT

There are two quite distinct ways of testing the Regge pole hypothesis by experiment. For example, consider nucleon-nucleon scattering. We know that in the channel where the c.m. energy is $\sqrt{s}$ corresponding to physical nucleon-nucleon scattering, there are Regge poles, one of them corresponding to the deuteron, for instance. Such a Regge pole has a direct physical meaning: it provides for binding of the deuteron. We shall say that this kind of physical interpretation takes place in the direct channel, in contradistinction with the crossed ones. In the crossed channels, which describe physical nucleon-antinucleon scattering, the deuteron Regge pole has a very different physical interpretation: it essentially contributes to the asymptotic behavior of the cross sections as a function of the energy (which is now $\sqrt{t}$ or $\sqrt{u}$, according to which way we cross). Experimental tests will therefore have two entirely different aspects, according to whether one tries to test Regge poles in the direct channel or in the crossed one.

8-1 EXPERIMENTAL TESTS IN THE DIRECT CHANNEL

The experimental tests in the direct channel are very poor. The idea is the following: each Regge pole must have well-defined quantum numbers, which are those of the particles or resonances to which it corresponds (baryon number, electric charge, isotopic spin, strangeness, parity, G parity). Classify all particles, stable or unstable, and resonances according to their quantum numbers and signature, that is, according to whether their spin is even or odd ($+\frac{1}{2}$ in the case of fermions). In each of the classes, try to see whether it is possible to arrange the particles on Regge pole trajectories. The only trouble is, as we shall see, that with the presently known elementary particles (that is, with small baryon number), there are only three classes which may possibly contain more than one particle, and there is not much information to be gained this way.

Let us see how this analysis is done:

We first take the bosons. Let us classify them according to their isotopic spin I and strangeness S, denoting by π the particles with $I = 1$, $S = 0$, by ω those with $I = 0$, $S = 0$, by K those with $I = \frac{1}{2}$, $S = 1$.

We then affix indices to represent parity and signature, in the following way:

Spin:	even		odd	
Parity:	+	−	−	+
Index:	α	β	γ	δ

For $S = 0$ we may add as upper index the sign of the G parity. We may list now the known particles, and only those having the same symbol and indices can belong to the same Regge pole.

Pion: π^-_β	η: ω^+_β	K: K_β
ρ: π^+_γ	ω: ω^-_γ	K^*_{885} : K_γ
	f_0: ω^+_α	

We see by examination that no set of quantum numbers has more than one representative.

We have at the present time more luck with the baryons: We use a notation whereby a baryon with $S = 0$, $I = \frac{1}{2}$ is denoted by N, with $S = 0$, $I = \frac{3}{2}$ by Δ, with $S = -1$, $I = 0$ by Λ, $S = -1$, $I = 1$ by Σ, and $S = -2$, $I = \frac{1}{2}$ by Ξ. We define as before a set of indices:

Spin:	$\frac{1}{2} + 2n$		$\frac{3}{2} + 2n$	
Parity:	+	−	−	+
Index:	α	β	γ	δ

The presently known particles are thus represented as:

Nucleon: N_α

2nd nucleon resonance: N_γ

3rd nucleon resonance: N_α

$\frac{3}{2}$, 3:2 (1st) nucleon resonance: Δ_δ

4th nucleon resonance: Δ_δ

Lambda: Λ_α

Sigma: Σ_α

$Y^*_{0\,(1520)}$: Λ_γ

$Y^*_{1\,(1385)}$: Σ_δ

$Y^{**}_{0\,(1815)}$: Λ_α

Cascade: Ξ_α

$\Xi^*_{1/2\,(1530)}$: Ξ_δ

The appended numerals are the masses of the unstable particles (in Mev) for identification purposes.

In some cases we have taken the most optimistic spin and parity, and still we have only three possible pairs of particles with the same symbols: N_α, Λ_α, and Δ_δ. If we really believe that each of these pairs lies on one Regge pole trajectory, then we may get an estimate of how fast the Regge poles are moving with energy. We thus get three *average* values of $d\alpha(s)/ds$, which fall remarkably close together at about 1 Gev^{-2}. This may very well be a coincidence, but at any rate it suggests the order of magnitude to be expected, at least for all strongly interacting particles. It might be used in some way to estimate in what region of energy to look for other excited baryons, starting from known low-energy baryons, and perhaps also for mesons.

8-2 EXPERIMENTAL TESTS IN THE CROSSED CHANNEL

The experimental tests in the crossed channels are, as we already said, linked with problems of asymptotic behavior of cross sections. Before entering the matter in more detail, we should like to emphasize two very important, although trivial, preliminary remarks.

The first remark is that, as crossing symmetry is a very specific feature of relativistic theory, nothing comparable to the physical consequences of Regge poles in the crossed channel can be envisioned in nonrelativistic potential scattering. Thus the tests we are proposing are tests not only of the Regge hypothesis but also of the whole idea of crossing, or possibly of some deeper idea, underlying both, and as yet unknown.

The second remark is that we can only test asymptotic behaviors. The question is very often asked: "When does one enter the asymptotic region?" The answer is that no theory presently known can give any clue to that question. To take a more concrete example, the kinetic theory of gases applies asymptotically to zero-pressure gases. It does not predict *a priori* when this asymptotic theory applies. It is up to the experimenter to take a gas and test the theory at lower and lower pressures until agreement with the theory is reached. This pressure will depend upon the particular gas and temperature. The experimenter may find that it works well with hydrogen under ordinary conditions but very poorly with carbon dioxide under the same conditions. In the latter case he may be obliged to use one-tenth of the initial pressure to find agreement. Of course, later refinements of the theory can predict what the deviations will be, and where the asymptotic region starts for each gas.

In the case of Regge pole theory, we have simply not yet reached this stage, and we shall have to carry on experimenting at higher and higher energies until the behavior appears to settle to what is expected.

8-3 TOTAL CROSS SECTIONS. THE POMERANCHUK POLE

We shall use first the simplest data available, the total cross sections, in order to get estimates on the forward amplitude through the optical theorem, (6-19).

Recall that we are dealing now with the crossed channel, that is, $\sqrt{t}$ is the total c.m. energy and s is the invariant momentum transfer variable. We have thus to use (6-19) by interchanging the variables t and s, and it reads

$$\text{Im } A(0,t) = \frac{k_t\sqrt{t}}{4\pi}\,\sigma_{tot}(t) \tag{8-1}$$

We take the asymptotic form for $k_t = \sqrt{t-4}/2 \simeq \sqrt{t}/2$ and get

$$\text{Im } A(0,t) \simeq \frac{t}{8\pi}\,\sigma_{tot}(t) \tag{8-2}$$

Now we compare with the Regge behavior as given by (7-10) or (7-11):

$$A(0,t) = \frac{\beta(0)}{\sin \Pi\alpha(0)}\left[P_{\alpha(0)}\left(-1 + \frac{2t}{4}\right) \pm P_{\alpha(0)}\left(1 - \frac{2t}{4}\right)\right] \tag{8-3}$$

$$A(0,t) \simeq \text{constant} \times t^{\alpha(0)} \tag{8-4}$$

We may suppose $\beta(0)$ real, like $\alpha(0)$. Then the phase of the constant in (8-4) depends only on the value of $\alpha(0)$ and the signature, being

$\pi\alpha(0)/2 + n\pi$ for + signature and $\pi[1 - \alpha(0)/2] + n\pi$ for − signature. We have of course taken only the dominant term, i.e., that with the largest Re α.

Comparing (8-2) and (8-4) we get

$$\sigma_{tot} \simeq \text{constant} \times t^{\alpha(0)-1} \qquad (8\text{-}5)$$

This is a powerful conclusion and allows one to determine the value $\alpha(0)$ at least for the leading pole. Experimentally, for all observed reactions, the total cross section goes to a constant, and if we conjecture that the asymptotic limit has been attained, then we can conclude that $\alpha(0) = 1$.

This leading pole has been named after Pomeranchuk, who first discussed, in an earlier context, the constancy of the cross section. Pomeranchuk showed, among other things, that such a pole could only have a + signature. In fact the − signature would give a real constant in (8-4), which would contradict (8-2).

It would now be very interesting to classify the Pomeranchuk pole according to the scheme of Sec. 8-2. We can do that by noticing that if s is the momentum-transfer variable for the elastic scattering of particles a and b then (Fig. 8-1) it is also the energy variable for the crossed reaction $b + \bar{b} \to a + \bar{a}$. In such a channel, all additive quantum numbers of the Pomeranchuk pole, which must be those of the system $a\bar{a}$ must vanish, as $\bar{a}$ has all these quantum numbers opposite to those of a. In particular the charge has only the value zero, which implies that it is an isotopic singlet $I = 0$. If we take a neutral pion as particle a, then $\bar{a}$ is also a π^0, and the G parity of the pole is therefore $G = +1$. Also, the possible physical states of two π^0 with even angular momentum (+ signature) have parity +1, owing to the symmetry of the wave function, and this completes the list of the quantum numbers of the Pomeranchuk pole. Therefore our Pomeranchuk pole is a boson pole, with symbol ω^+ and index α.

Therefore we can represent the contribution of the Pomeranchuk pole to forward scattering in more detail than in Fig. 8-1, as shown in Fig. 8-2. We say that the large scattering amplitude in the

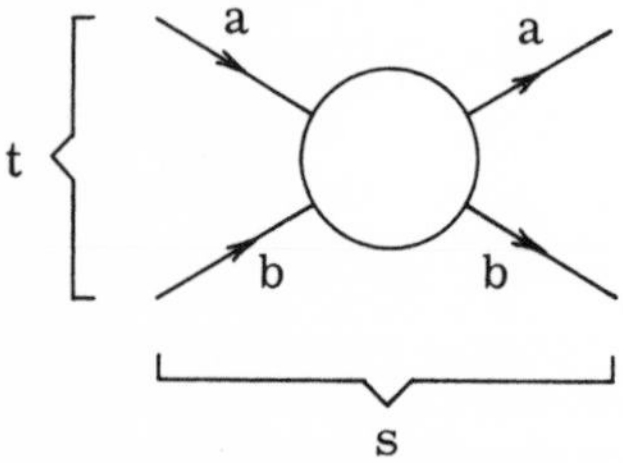

Figure 8-1

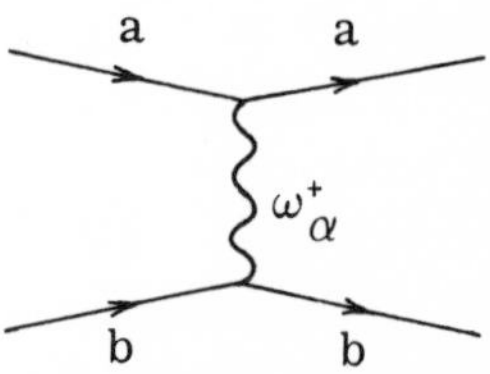

Figure 8-2

forward direction is due to the exchange of the Pomeranchuk pole, or particle.

We notice that we have already met a particle of type ω_α^+ in the list of Sec. 8-1: the f^0 particle. Thus it would be acceptable to take it as located on the same trajectory as the Pomeranchuk pole. It would lead to an average $d\alpha/ds$ of 0.6 Gev^{-2}, of the same order of magnitude as those found for the baryons.

We can now exploit another feature of the Regge pole hypothesis. Equation (8-3) shows that the total cross section is proportional to $\beta(0)$. But we have seen in (7-12) that $\beta(0)$ is the product of two terms which depend on a and b only, as $a\bar{a}$ and $b\bar{b}$ are in the incoming and outgoing channels when $\sqrt{s}$ is the c.m. energy (see Fig. 8-2, sideways). So we have

$$\sigma_{\text{tot}}^{(a+b)} = X^a \cdot X^b$$

It is easy to determine X^a by

$$\sigma_{\text{tot}}^{(a+b)} = (X^a)^2$$

So we get finally

$$\sigma_{\text{tot}}^{(a+b)} = \left[\sigma_{\text{tot}}^{(a+a)} \times \sigma_{\text{tot}}^{(b+b)}\right]^{1/2} \tag{8-6}$$

We have of course here to take the limit values of the total cross sections as the energy goes to infinity.

At any rate, some of these limit cross sections appear to be fairly well known, such as nucleon-nucleon or pion-nucleon, but we do not have the limiting value of the pion-pion cross section, which we can predict to be about

$$\frac{\left(\sigma_{\text{tot}}^{\pi N}\right)^2}{\sigma_{\text{tot}}^{NN}} \approx 15 \text{ mb}$$

All the predictions of this kind are impossible to test, as long as the only available target is the nucleon.

8-4 TOTAL CROSS SECTIONS. THE SATELLITE POLES

We have considered in Sec. 8-3 only the leading pole for the evaluation of the total cross section. One may be more precise, taking instead of (8-5) the contribution of several poles (we take all $\alpha_i(0)$ real, for simplicity):

$$\sigma_{tot}^{a+b} \simeq \sum_i C_i t^{\alpha_i(0)-1} \tag{8-7}$$

If η_i is the signature of the i-th pole, then, we may relate σ_{tot}^{a+b} to $\sigma_{tot}^{a+\bar{b}}$, by crossing the b and $\bar{b}$ legs of Fig. 8-1. The crossing operation will change the coefficient C_i into $\eta_i C_i$, as changing b into $\bar{b}$ simply changes the sign of $\cos\,\theta_s$. We thus have

$$\sigma_{tot}^{a+\bar{b}} = \sum_i \eta_i C_i t^{\alpha_i(0)-1} \tag{8-8}$$

We check that the leading term, the Pomeranchuk, has $\eta = +1$ and therefore does not change sign, which would give a negative cross section.

Comparison of (8-7) and (8-8) allows us to separate the poles with different signatures. For example, consider proton-proton and proton-antiproton total cross sections. They behave as indicated by Fig. 8-3.

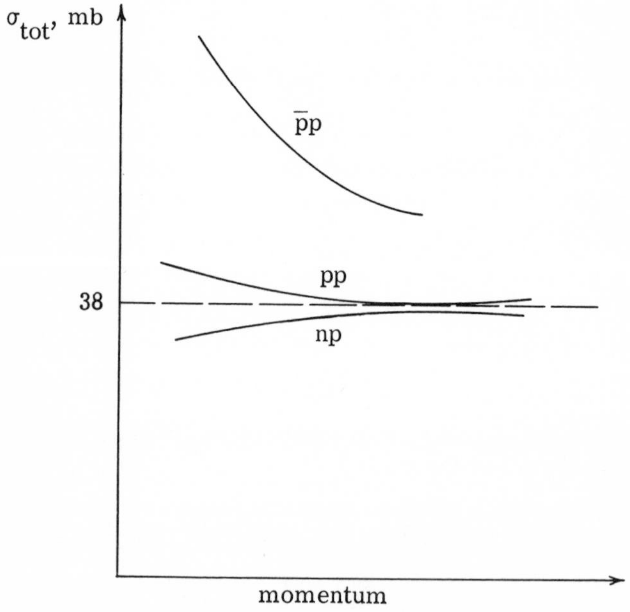

Figure 8-3

The difference $\sigma^{\bar{p}p} - \sigma^{pp}$ comes from poles with signature −1 and the corresponding α is, as estimated from the curve, of the order of 0.4. The only two known particles with signature −1, near enough to zero mass, are the ρ and ω mesons. But the ρ meson has isotopic spin one, and therefore does not contribute much, as it would introduce a large difference between the neutron-proton and proton-proton cross sections. Hence the only candidate is the ω meson, with a trajectory ω_{γ}^{-}, and $\alpha(0) \approx 0.4$.

The sum of the cross sections $\sigma^{\bar{p}p} + \sigma^{pp}$ does not go very fast to the high-energy limit. Indeed, as the pp cross section reaches the limit very quickly, the sum $\sigma^{\bar{p}p} + \sigma^{pp}$ and the difference $\sigma^{\bar{p}p} - \sigma^{pp}$ reach their limits in almost the same way. There must be therefore a pole with signature +1, which approximately cancels the ω pole in pp scattering, and adds with it in $p\bar{p}$ scattering.

This pole, sometimes denoted by P′, does not correspond to any identified particle. It would also have $\alpha(0) \approx 0.4$, and about the same coupling strength as the ω. (It is of course ω_{α}^{+}, like the Pomeranchuk pole.)

8-5 THE DIFFRACTION PEAK

There is a lot more information to be gained about the Regge poles by looking at differential cross sections, but the experiments are correspondingly more difficult. We study in this section the largest differential cross section at high energies, that is, the elastic. It is large, because it is essentially diffraction scattering, as treated in Section 6-2. We obtain the value of the differential cross section from (1-4) and (6-5) as

$$\frac{d\sigma^{el}}{d\Omega} = \frac{1}{t} \, |A(s,t)|^2$$

We are still in the channel were $\sqrt{t}$ is the total c.m. energy and $\cos\theta_t \approx 1 + (2s/t)$, whence $d\Omega_t = (4\overline{\Lambda}/t)\, ds$. We can thus compute

$$\frac{d\sigma^{el}}{ds} = \frac{4\Pi}{t^2} \, |A(s,t)|^2 \tag{8-9}$$

If we put the leading pole contribution in place of A(s,t), we get

$$\frac{d\sigma^{el}}{ds} = g^2(s)\, t^{2[\alpha(s)-1]} \tag{8-10}$$

This allows in principle a measurement of $\alpha(s)$. The sequence of operations would be to measure $d\sigma/ds$, at a given value of s for ever-increasing values of t. Then plot (Fig. 8-4) the $\ln(d\sigma/ds)$ versus $\ln t$, up to such large values of t that the curve becomes straight. The asymptote to the curve is the straight line:

$$\ln \frac{d\sigma^{el}}{ds} = \ln g^2(s) + 2[\alpha(s) - 1] \ln t$$

This furnishes a measurement of g(s) and $\alpha(s)$, which may be repeated in principle for all negative (physical) values of s. The experiment is in practice very difficult for the following reasons: (1) It is difficult to reach large values of $\ln t$; (2) the laboratory scattering angle corresponding to constant s varies like $1/t$; (3) the differential cross section to be measured goes down very fast; (4) it is hard to recognize when a curve has "reached" its asymptote.

Nevertheless, preliminary experiments have been carried on and have given some results. Elastic proton-proton scattering has been studied extensively in that respect, and the Pomeranchuk pole appears to be trackable down to values of s of the order of -1 Gev^2, and values of α in the vicinity of zero, which would again confirm the general trend of results on the average $d\alpha/ds \approx 1$ Gev^2. Preliminary results on elastic pion-nucleon scattering have been less optimistic, but, again, it is hard to draw any definite conclusions as long as the experiments are made with the present 30-Gev accelerators.

An interesting question arises when tracking the Pomeranchuk trajectory down to large values of $|s|$: Does $\alpha(s)$ reach the value 0, and, if so, what happens there? Of course it may happen that $\alpha(s)$

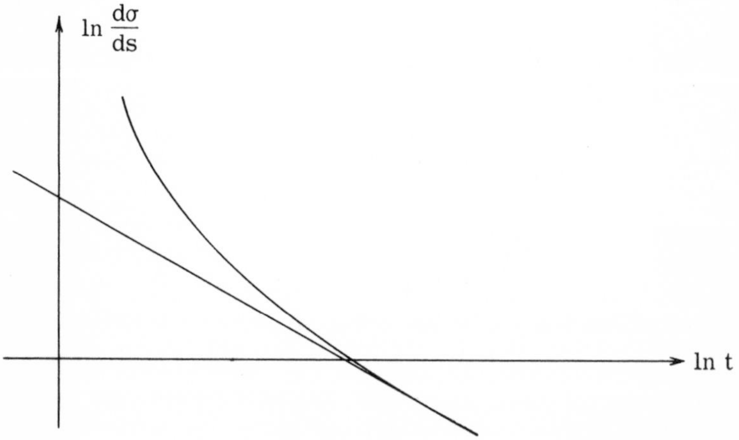

Figure 8-4

always stays between 0 and 1, and this does not present any particular difficulty. But if it crosses the value 0, as the signature of the Pomeranchuk pole is +1, it should give rise to a pole (ghost). This is physically absurd, as a pole at a value $s = s_0$ corresponds to a particle with mass $\sqrt{s_0}$. For $s_0 < 0$ it corresponds to a particle with imaginary mass, that is, with space-like momentum. It is then easy to show that no system has a ground state, as the sum of space-like momenta may have an arbitrary large negative time-component. The whole world would decay into these strange things, unless, of course, the coupling vanishes. And this is what probably occurs: $\beta(s)$ goes through zero, so that $\beta(s)/\sin \Pi\alpha(s)$ stays bounded (7-10). This does not appear to be an accident, but rather quite a frequent phenomenon, although it is not completely clear yet exactly how it happens. It has been observed on model theories, and perhaps also shows up with the particles with large ground-state spins (deformed nuclei).

Before leaving the subject of the diffraction peak, we would like to come back to the semiclassical representation we have mentioned in Sec. 7-2. The peak we are dealing with now is a shrinking peak, in the sense that one can write (8-10) in the form:

$$\frac{d\sigma^{el}}{ds} = g^2(s)\, e^{2[(\partial\alpha/\partial s) \ln t]s}$$

As t increases, the exponential beats $g^2(s)$, being more and more damped $(s < 0)$. The width, in s, of the diffraction peak goes down as $1/\ln t$. The total elastic cross section is

$$\int_{-\infty}^{0} \frac{d\sigma^{el}}{ds}\, ds \simeq \frac{g^2(0)}{2\frac{\partial\alpha}{\partial s}\ln t} \to 0$$

The width in s of the diffraction peak is related to the width in laboratory angle by

$$\theta_{lab} \approx \frac{2m\sqrt{-s}}{t}$$

The effective radius of the target is

$$R \approx \frac{1}{P_{lab}\theta_{lab}} \approx \frac{2m}{t}\,\frac{t}{2m\sqrt{-s}} \approx \frac{1}{\sqrt{-s}} \approx \sqrt{\ln t}$$

It increases indefinitely as the energy increases while the total cross section keeps constant. Everything looks as if the target blows out like a puff of smoke as the energy increases, becoming more and more transparent. It is a rather odd picture, which is worth establishing definitely from experiment.

8-6 THE INELASTIC EXPERIMENTS

Inelastic scattering is presumably even more difficult to measure than the elastic one, as we cannot count on the diffraction to keep the cross sections high. However, it has been noticed that slightly inelastic scattering could take place in measurable amount in some conditions. The idea is the following. Take for definiteness proton-proton scattering. Then suppose we modify the diagram of Fig. 8-2 by replacing one of the final protons by an excited proton N^* (Fig. 8-5), which may subsequently decay as it likes to. If the exchanged pole is a Pomeranchuk pole, there probably will be a large cross section, large enough at least to be detectable. If, on the other hand, because of some conservation law, the Pomeranchuk pole cannot be exchanged, then we would expect the particular reaction cross section to go down quite fast. This could be realized by exciting a Δ resonance ($I = \frac{3}{2}$); as the Pomeranchuk has $I = 0$, it is forbidden. The experiments are conducted in the following way: the momentum of the outgoing proton is carefully measured, and the mass M^2 corresponding to the missing momentum computed. The differential cross section $d\sigma/dM^2$ is then computed. It shows a large peak at elastic scattering. Then there are two small bumps corresponding pretty closely to the 2nd and 3rd nucleon resonances (N_γ and N_α) as far as the value of M^2 is concerned. There is no trace of the 1st and 4th resonances (Δ_δ), except at very low energy for the 1st resonance. It is difficult to draw definite conclusions from this particular experiment, as the background is very large as compared to the particular reactions under consideration.

Other kinds of experiments could be done to test, for example, whether the Regge form for one-nucleon exchange is better than the ordinary perturbation calculation. More specifically, one could try to measure the backward pion-nucleon scattering (Fig. 8-6) and see whether the value of α changes from its value $\frac{1}{2}$ at the nucleon pole or not.

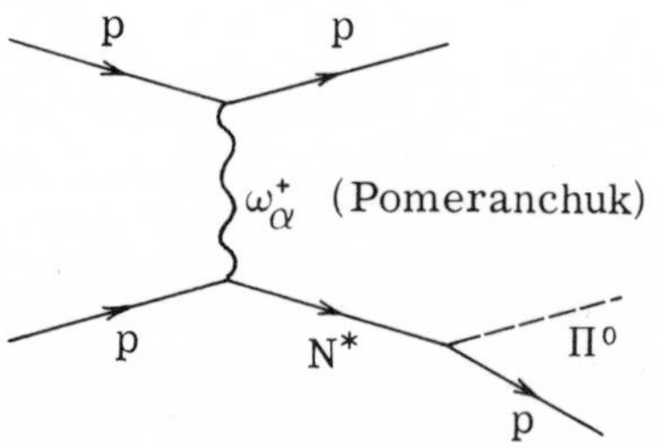

Figure 8-5

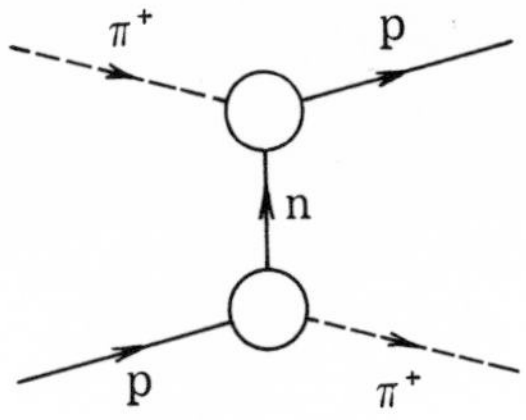

Figure 8-6

Such an experiment would be done in the following way: The differential scattering cross section is measured asymptotically for high energies, keeping the crossed momentum transfer fixed. This would determine a value of α corresponding to the first baryon Regge pole. Conventional perturbation theory would lead to α constant and equal to $\frac{1}{2}$, the spin of the nucleon. If the measured value goes down below $\frac{1}{2}$, then it would be a success of the Regge pole theory against conventional theories. It would be a very interesting confirmation of the Regge pole theory, because it would test if Chew's hypothesis holds for small values of ℓ, less than one, for which the unitarity limit does not hold any more.

BIBLIOGRAPHY

A more complete treatment of the Mandelstam representation with applications to physical problems, together with some important original articles and a rather complete bibliography may be found in G. F. Chew, "S-Matrix Theory of Strong Interactions," Benjamin, New York, 1961.

For the study of nonrelativistic scattering, introductory articles are: A. Martin, *Nuovo Cimento, Suppl.*, **21**, 157 (1961). T. Regge, either in "Theoretical Physics," AIEA, Vienna, 1963, or in "Lectures on High Energy Physics at Hercegnovi," Federal Nuclear Energy Commission of Yugoslavia, 1961.

The original proposal of extending Regge results to relativistic problems is given in G. F. Chew and S. C. Frautschi, *Phys. Rev. Letters*, **8**, 41 (1962), and the necessary methods worked out in M. Gell-Mann, S. C. Frautschi, and F. Zachariasen, *Phys. Rev.*, **126**, 2204 (1962).

A numerical study of Regge poles trajectories in the nonrelativistic problem is given by A. Ahmadzadeh, P. Burke, and C. Tate, *UCRL Rept.*, **10-216**.

For more recent results see the reports by G. Cocconi and S. D. Drell in the "Proceedings of the 1962 Conference in High-Energy Physics," CERN (Rochester), 1962.

INDEX